THE BRIDGING OF TROY

The Bridging of Troy

or

Tales from the Trojan Tournament

by

CHRIS ACKERLEY

LONDON
VICTOR GOLLANCZ LTD
in association with Peter Crawley
1986

First published in Great Britain 1986
by Victor Gollancz Ltd,
14 Henrietta Street, London WC2E 8QJ

© Chris Ackerley 1986

British Library Cataloguing in Publication Data
Ackerley, Chris
    The bridging of Troy.—(Master bridge series)
    1. Contract bridge—Anecdotes, facetiae, satire, etc.
    I. Title   II. Series
    795.41'5'0207   GV1282.32

ISBN 0-575-03812-8

For David

Photoset in Great Britain by
Photobooks (Bristol) Ltd.
Printed by WBC Print Ltd., Bristol

Invocation

Sing, Muse, etc. Diomedes, son of Tydeus, at your service. Place: the wind-swept halls of Menelaus in Sparta. Time: four and twenty years after the Fall of Troy. There's not many of us left now – Achilles brought to heel, Agamemnon's got the chop, Odysseus last heard of somewhere beyond the Pillars of Hercules. As for the rest of us:

> We're old and we're grey,
> We're wasting away,
> All our tomorrows
> Are yesterdays.

Old players losing their pips and fading out, opponents getting younger every year. Ah, we had fire in our bellies once – now, twice the belly, half the fire. Old anecdotage, they call it: finesses no longer working, suits not quite adding up to thirteen, muddles and puddles. . .

"Why me?" I wondered when they suggested writing up the records. "Why not?" they replied. It seems that young Aeneas, who got away from Troy and set up his club in Rome, is about to publish his memoirs and his version of things (*Timeo Danaos et dona ferentes*) isn't all that flattering to our side. Besides, I was the only one of us left who could read or write. So I put Pegasus to the plough and dug deep into my mind:

> Declare, O Muse, in what ill-fated hour
> Sprang the fierce strife, for what offended power.

And so on. And so forth. "No good," they cried. "Couplets are passé, stick to plain old Linear B, and never mind the slips that pass in the type. And tell us all about Helen. . ."

Ah, Helen! Helen of Troy, the once and future Helen of Sparta! As we sit here in these draughty halls, by the still hearth, among these barren crags, far from the ringing plains of windy Troy, watching Helen getting supper for the boys – why, it's impossible to remember the drunken delight of past tournaments, to imagine this grey-haired grandmother as the grey-eyed girl who started it all, to recall the fire that stirred about her when she stirred. Contracts bidden and broken, partner-ships wrecked, a thousand cold bottoms on the ocean's. Ai, how the years go by. . .

Catalogue

I

The Parisian Finesse

Note: Paris, having judged Aphrodite the fairest of goddesses, was to be rewarded by her with the fairest of mortals, and sailed from Troy to Greece, where he was hospitably received by Menelaus, King of Sparta. Helen, wife of Menelaus, was the woman destined for Paris. She had been sought by many, but before her decision was known her suitors swore to accept her choice, to defend her from injury, and to avenge her if she were wronged. For reasons incomprehensible to many, Helen's choice was Menelaus; but Paris persuaded her to go with him to Troy, and thereby initiated the Trojan Wars. Yet why Helen so readily agreed to go has hitherto remained a mystery. . .

We had all wanted to be her partner, but had agreed among ourselves to respect her choice, even if it were Menelaus. It was. We wished them well, and all remained so till wandering Paris wound his way to our walls. He was doing the Grand Tour, he told us, visiting the ancient club-houses of Egypt and Babylonia, learning new systems, and generally getting plastered. Only later did we learn that Priam, noting a few too many protean deals and left-handed leads, had sent Paris and his partner to follow awhile the good winds ("Buenos Aires," he had remarked, somewhat cryptically). But at the time they seemed likely lads, and Menelaus, taken in, had taken them in. They hung around the club-house for a week or two, giving the inside story of what had happened at Mount Ida, and doing well out of increasingly aggrieved opponents who couldn't understand why the cards were suddenly so unlucky.

[9]

They were good players, mind you, were Paris and Minos, and nobody could actually prove anything. And Helen of the lovely hair wouldn't listen to a word against them. "Nonsense," she would say. "One of them may be a Cretan, but they're not all liars, and as for Paris. . ." Her voice would trail off, but the warmth of her tone presaged heat and friction. And Menelaus, who had always been a bit wet, was not the one to quench her fires.

Paris made it worse with his poetry. "My bella donna," he would call her, praising in one both her bridge and her beauty; and then he would cite those mighty lines about the face that launched a thousand ships and burnt the topless towers of Ilium. It was an obvious invitation for her to immolate herself upon his fiery tower, and finding that we had started to call her 'Topless Helen' only added resin to his torch.

Something had to be done, and it was your humble scribe who came up with the bright idea at duplicate that evening. Odysseus had come over for the game, and we were sitting North-South at the table which passed the boards on to Menelaus and doddery old Atreus. Helen, like a dutiful wife and daughter-in-law, sat next to her husband, but her grey eyes were on Paris and Minos, next comers to their table. We had just finished Board 13, playing in four spades like everybody else, and holding ourselves to four by finessing clubs the wrong way. Looking at the hand, I suddenly realised that Paris and Minos would play it next, and that their Cretan Club system included the Mendacious Two Diamonds: Minos would open, and Paris would end up playing the hand. Here was our chance to reveal their lack of ethics, to make a fool of Paris, and to give Menelaus (with Helen watching) the chance to be a hero! As quick as Zeus's thunderbolt I wondered aloud, in a voice just carrying to Paris of the sharp ears and fingers, "How come nobody's bid the Grand in spades? As the cards lie, it's frigid." I saw the head of Paris flicker, and Odysseus, brighter than a shower of golden rain, glanced up and added, "It's the void. People simply don't know how to handle them." And he gave me the hint of a wink as we passed on the board with these four dubious hands:

Board 13
All Vulnerable

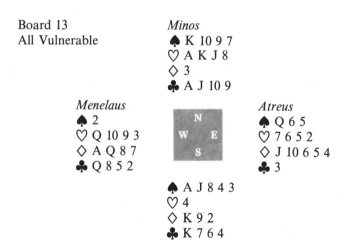

Minos
♠ K 10 9 7
♡ A K J 8
◇ 3
♣ A J 10 9

Menelaus
♠ 2
♡ Q 10 9 3
◇ A Q 8 7
♣ Q 8 5 2

Atreus
♠ Q 6 5
♡ 7 6 5 2
◇ J 10 6 5 4
♣ 3

♠ A J 8 4 3
♡ 4
◇ K 9 2
♣ K 7 6 4
Paris

Obviously, the grand slam is as remote as Colchis: not only may the ace of diamonds be cashed, but there is a probable loser in spades, a guess in clubs, and all kinds of potential blockages and communications problems. We heard with delight the following sequence, which seemed to confirm that not only Cretans are liars:

West	North	East	South
	2◇	Pass	2♡
Double	Redouble	Pass	2NT
Double	Redouble	3◇	4◇
Double	Redouble	Pass	7♠
Pass	Pass	Pass	

Atreus was completely lost, Menelaus equally so; and Paris sneeringly informed them that the opening two diamonds showed either a Weak Two in a major, or a Cretan 4-4-4-1/4-4-5-0 hand with 16+ points; that two hearts requested partner to pass if that were his suit; that the first REDOUBLE confirmed 16+ with hearts; that two no trumps asked for more information; that the second REDOUBLE presumably showed an even bigger hand; that the third REDOUBLE had to show first round control in diamonds ("We spell 'Cretan' with an alpha, not an iota," he added); and that seven spades was the first honest bid ("Grabbing the bull by the horns," Minos commented). Paris also expressed his regrets that the pattern of doubles and REDOUBLES had not been repeated.

[11]

So Menelaus was on lead against the Grand (with Helen watching). Determined to be the hero and not the goat, he knew better than to lead an ace against a freely-bid slam, especially when the void had been confirmed by the bidding. Nor did it look right to lead from either queen. He therefore led his singleton trump.

That took care of the first finesse. Paris won the queen of spades with the ace; immediately took the club finesse; then played off spades, ending in hand. And when the last trump was played, it sounded to Menelaus like the knell of Judgement Day:

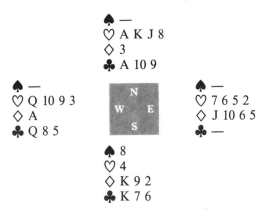

```
                    ♠ —
                    ♡ A K J 8
                    ◇ 3
                    ♣ A 10 9
    ♠ —                              ♠ —
    ♡ Q 10 9 3        N              ♡ 7 6 5 2
    ◇ A          W         E         ◇ J 10 6 5
    ♣ Q 8 5          S              ♣ —
                    ♠ 8
                    ♡ 4
                    ◇ K 9 2
                    ♣ K 7 6
```

Squeezed to the bones, Menelaus threw the ace of diamonds (dummy unblocking a club); but when Paris produced Old Cyclops all was lost. Menelaus threw a club, but Paris played one to the ace; and then another back to the king, dropping the queen; he then cashed the last club and finessed the hearts. Seven spades making, played by Paris (with Helen watching), on three finesses and a squeeze.

The rest is history. There was a clash of falling chairs, prefiguring that of toppling towers, as Helen threw her arms around the neck of Paris, who rose to his feet in triumphant scorn and led her from the room and Sparta. Thrice-finessed Menelaus sat as one stunned, his wife and cards scattered to the good winds. In vain did we pour him comforting libations, threaten to drown the Cretan in a Minoan undulation, remind him that 'belladonna' also meant 'deadly nightshade'. In vain, in vain. Only when Agamemnon promised to launch the thousand ships and burn the topless towers did Menelaus stretch one hand towards Olympus and the gods, and swear a terrible metaphor: "I will to Troy. Almighty Zeus, if there be in my vengeance any spark of life, I pray thee, water that spark." Battle had begun.

[12]

II

Iphigenia's Sacrifice

Note: The Greek forces were assembled on the shore at Aulis, ready
to embark for Troy, but were unable to depart because the
gods had withheld the winds. Calchas, the soothsayer, consulted the Oracle to discover that the gods were displeased
because Agamemnon had offended Artemis by shooting one
of her sacred deer. They would be propitiated only by the
sacrifice of Iphigenia, daughter of Agamemnon and Clytemnestra. Agamemnon reluctantly agreed to the sacrifice, and
sent for Iphigenia on the pretext of marrying her to Achilles.
The sacrifice took place, but even though Artemis may have
rescued Iphigenia and taken her to Tauris a lasting rift opened
between Agamemnon and Clytemnestra; and on Agamemnon's
return years later he was slain in his bath by Clytemnestra and
her lover Aegisthus. Such stories, of course, are an allegorical
rendering of what really happened. . .

We were sitting on the shore, watching the waves and waiting for
the winds to waft us eastwards to Troy, when who should turn up but
that old battleaxe, Clytemnestra, accompanied as usual by goaty
Aegisthus. They'd brought with them young Iphigenia – seems she's
got a crush on Achilles and hoped for a chance to hold his hand.
Iphy's a nice kid, but she's only just learning the basics of both games.
Anyway, Clytie insisted on a special general meeting, and she sure
had plenty to say: we were told in no uncertain terms that
Agamemnon had sneaked off without so much as a fare-thee-well,
that it was his turn to look after little Orestes, and that he'd been
allowed to go shooting last week-end only on condition that she'd be
playing in the next tournament. In other words, she should be going
and he staying.

At first we thought she was joking, and laughter rang out, but
Clytemnestra held firm. Agamemnon, mightiest of men and slayer of
heroes, fell like a fig. We protested that he was our king, that the lofty
ridge of Troy would fall before his trumpet, that having our non-
playing captain five hundred miles away didn't make sense. In vain.
She could take his place, she insisted; she would even be captain. And,
she pleaded persuasively, since the object of the enterprise was to get

[13]

Helen back, would not a woman's, nay, a sister's touch be more effective? Moreover, she finished triumphantly, it was clearly the wish of the gods that she should play, or else we'd have been off ages ago.

It was an impasse. We gazed at the waiting ships, but their sails were as limp as Agamemnon. We consulted Calchas, who in turn consulted the Oracle, which issued forth this majestic utterance:

> *Many bold women praises slaughter slaughter*
> *Brings rout this strumpet pleads least she*
> *Plays this bridge she burns his boats*

A cry of triumph went up from the Clytemnestra faction at this clear statement of her apparent right to play. But Odysseus nudged me, and asked if I'd noticed anything odd about the phrasing.

"Odd?" I said slowly. "Not exactly odd. Ungrammatical, yes. Dionysius Thrax wouldn't like 'women praises', but that's about all."

"Precisely," said Odysseus. "Oracles are never wrong. Ambiguous, yes, but ungrammatical, never. Think about it." But before I could he had clapped me on the shoulder, and moved to the Tripod to address the assembly.

"It seems to me," he began in his usual persuasive way, "that the issue is not (as it were) so clear. The gods have spoken, true, but their words are often dark, and 'strumpet' is not an unequivocal term of praise. And let us remember Croesus: the Oracle told him that by crossing the Halys he would a great kingdom destroy, and, poor fool, it turned out to be his own. Personally, I'm afraid that if Clytemnestra leads us the 'slaughter brings rout' bit might backfire. I suggest that to clarify the will of the gods Clytemnestra and Agamemnon should play off, the winner to lead us against Troy."

His words were acclaimed, and the match set up. Clytemnestra and Aegisthus were to play Agamemnon and a player selected by lot, thirteen boards to be IMPed against par, with Calchas as absolute arbiter. Achilles passed round his helmet, and all who were willing to play placed in it some kind of personal token. The draw was made, and a strange silence fell as Calchas pulled out Iphigenia's charm bracelet.

Agamemnon took it well, all things considered. Calchas offered another draw, on the grounds that since Iphigenia wouldn't be going to Troy she shouldn't be eligible (it seemed she'd been unable to resist Achilles as he passed by); but Agamemnon declared that if the Fates had decreed that his devoted daughter be his partner, he was not one to say them nay. A noble gesture, since her play was decidedly iffy.

[14]

Calchas dealt the hands, submitted them to the Oracle to determine par, and play began – one lone table on the strand beneath Apollo's golden arrows, the assembled might of Achaia looking on. The first few boards were as flat as Cassandra, as games were bid and made for no pick-up at all. But then Agamemnon, trying to shield Iphigenia from danger, played in no trumps instead of hearts, and went down. A little later he lost out on a part-score, and then Iphigenia failed to cash a winner and went down in a cold contract. It looked like a slaughter, a rout, but in desperation Agamemnon bid four spades and made it when par was only two. Even so, when the last board was taken from the shrine he and Iphigenia were eleven IMPs down. Only Odysseus seemed strangely unmoved as the players took out their final hands, all vulnerable:

Board 13
All Vulnerable

Aegisthus
♠ 5
♡ A 6
◊ A J 7 6 3 2
♣ A Q 9 2

Agamemnon
♠ 8 7 4 3
♡ J 8 7 2
◊ —
♣ K 8 7 6 4

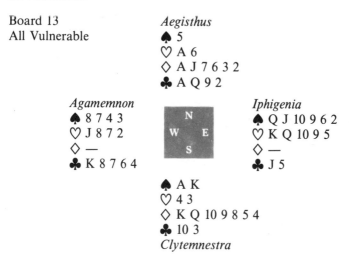

Iphigenia
♠ Q J 10 9 6 2
♡ K Q 10 9 5
◊ —
♣ J 5

♠ A K
♡ 4 3
◊ K Q 10 9 8 5 4
♣ 10 3
Clytemnestra

Agamemnon's face registered dismay as he picked up his hand, but dismay changed to epic perplexity as Aegisthus opened One Delphic Diamond (which could be short), and Iphigenia bid two diamonds. When asked what that meant, Agamemnon suddenly realised that they were playing both a natural overcall over the ambiguous diamond, and the Mycenaean cue-bid to show both majors. Playing Nemesis doubles Clytemnestra was happy to pass, and after infinite agonising (she must have diamonds!) Agamemnon did the same. Aegisthus, eleven IMPs up and on the last hand, saw no reason to disturb the hopeless contract, and Iphigenia was left to play two diamonds in her 0–0 fit.

[15]

The play was simple. Clytemnestra led the king of spades, and when she switched to the king of trumps it was as easy as pi to take all thirteen tricks. Agamemnon had slumped to the sand at the second trick, and seemed barely to register the fact that Iphigenia had gone down eight tricks vulnerable.

There was a hush as Calchas read out the Oracle's ruling: with seven diamonds making North–South, par was decreed to be seven spades doubled by East–West, off five, 1400 to North–South – a difference of 600 on the actual score; hence, twelve IMPs to Agamemnon, and game, set and match to him by one.

When Agamemnon heard this ruling, he raised his head from the sand in total disbelief. Then he scrambled to his feet, kissed Iphigenia in a most unpaternal manner, rammed Achilles's helmet upon his head, and rushed down to the ships, where the first faint breezes were already ruffling the sails. With a loud cry we followed, leaving Aegisthus and Clytemnestra staring in disbelief and mutual recrimination at the cards now scattered on the sands. And as we ran towards the wine-dark sea, I asked Odysseus why he had been so confident.

"Faith, m'boy, faith," he chuckled. "No chicanery here, as you might say. Zeus weaves mysterious mazes, but his shuttle is sure. The Oracle clearly prophesied the triumph of Agamemnon, but it was good for his morale as well as everybody else's that he should prove himself this way."

"What do you mean, the Oracle 'clearly prophesied'?" I scoffed.

"Try dropping the first letter of each word," Odysseus suggested. I did so, and stopped in disbelief:

Any old omen raises laughter laughter
Rings out his trumpet leads east he
Lays his ridge he urns 'is oats

"But what about 'urns'?" I asked. "And topless 'is'? I thought you said the Oracle doesn't make mistakes?"

"That's the other reason I couldn't bring it out openly," admitted Odysseus. "There's a further prophecy behind that last phrase, with 'urns' obviously meaning 'burial urns': if you fiddle with those letters you'll get 'RUINS TO ASHES'. In my opinion, it doesn't look too good for Agamemnon in the home stretch. You know Clytie – Iphigenia won't be welcome back at Mycenae after this, and it's a doris to a drachma that Agamemnon's going to find himself in hot water when he gets back. Let's just leave it at that."

[16]

III

The Judgement of Paris

Note: How it all began: although Eris (Strife) had not been invited to the wedding of Peleus and Thetis, the parents of Achilles, she turned up all the same, and created Discord by throwing among the guests an apple inscribed 'To the Fairest'. Hera, Athena and Aphrodite each claimed the apple for herself, and Paris, a shepherd on the slopes of Mount Ida, was called upon to judge which of the three had best claim to the title. Hera offered Paris wisdom and power, Athena victory in war, and Aphrodite Helen of Troy. Paris, smitten by the vision of loveliness, awarded the apple to Aphrodite, incurring her favour but thereby earning the lasting enmity of the other goddesses. Paris was obviously confronted with an impossible choice, but the complete account of what happened at the critical moment has not, as it were, been revealed. . .

'Twas on the good ship *Aphrodite* – by Zeus, you should have seen us! Our canvas bellying to the fair wind, and our rowers, hungry-looking, leaning into their oars and sending us scudding Troywards across Poseidon's fishy fields. We had just finished our spell of duty, and were lying in the late afternoon sun on the stern deck, pleasantly pooped.

"But what I don't understand," said ill-fated Protesilaus, breaking in upon our reveries, "is why we've kept the name *Aphrodite*. Isn't she supposed to be helping the Trojans?"

"Two reasons," grunted Odysseus, leaning back against the mast and reaching into the apple-barrel. "For one thing, it's bad luck to change a ship's name, and for another the goddess is unlikely to take direct action against a ship bearing her name."

"But," persisted Protesilaus, "I still don't understand why she's got it in for us. What have we ever done to her?"

"It's a long story," began Odysseus. "And a rather petty one at that. But as great Alexander sings:

> What dire Offence from am'rous Causes springs,
> What mighty Contests rise from trivial Things.

[17]

It all goes back to the time that Peleus and Thetis – Achilles's agèd P's, you know – held a Teams-of-Four evening. Eris hadn't been invited to play, but turned up like a bad fury all the same, with a trophy inscribed 'For the Champion'. Well, at the end of the evening, as captain of the winning team, Hera reached for the trophy as her natural right, only to have her claim disputed by Athena and Aphrodite, who were also on the winning side. From then on things got rather catty, and the fur began to fly. In the end they appealed to Zeus, but he wasn't having any of it, thank you, and suggested that they should play off among themselves for the title.

"So, one fine summer's day Hermes led the three of them to Mount Ida, where a table had been set up and Paris ditto. The idea was that they'd play the same thirteen-board game three times, with Paris fixed as South, and the goddesses each taking turns at North, East, and West. Between sessions there'd be meals provided, nectar and ambrosia and the usual, but also Lethe water and poppies of Morpheus so that they could forget the hands just played. That way Paris would be able to compare the results board for board, and decide upon the winner.

"Why Paris, you may well ask?

A mind and character so ordinary
albeit a prince
and brought up as a shepherd. . .

Nothing particularly distinguished about him. The usual heroic background, of course: prophecies of doom – his mother dreamt she was giving birth to a flaming torch – exposure at birth, suckled by a she-bear, and so on. Nothing really startling. He spent most of his time looking after his sheep, strumming his lyre, and composing bad strophes about love and peacocks, glory and vast herds:

The mountain sheep are sweeter,
But the valley sheep are fatter;
We therefore deemed it meeter
To carry off the latter.

That sort of thing. But he'd come to Priam's attention when he and Oenone had come from nowhere to win the Trojan Pairs, and he seemed to be the right man for the job.

"And so the game got under way. Paris and Hera against Aphrodite and Athena in the first round; pause for poppies; then Paris and Athena against Hera and Aphrodite. Curious situation,

[18]

with none of them able to remember how they'd done earlier. But it wasn't until the evening session that anything happened. The goddesses had retired to the sacred springs to do whatever goddesses have to do, and when they came back foamy Aphrodite was wearing the most transparent chiton that Paris had ever seen.

"For twelve boards they, sorry, she, sat opposite him in the moonlight, and it was with the greatest of difficulty that Paris was able to keep his eyes and mind on his cards. Thoughts of Oenone banished forever. Then came the last board, all vulnerable, with Aphrodite to open the bidding." Odysseus scribbled the hands upon the deck:

Board 13
All vulnerable

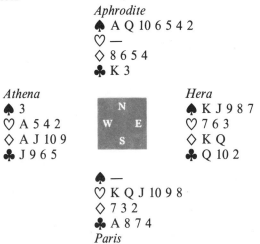

Aphrodite
♠ A Q 10 6 5 4 2
♡ —
◇ 8 6 5 4
♣ K 3

Athena
♠ 3
♡ A 5 4 2
◇ A J 10 9
♣ J 9 6 5

Hera
♠ K J 9 8 7
♡ 7 6 3
◇ K Q
♣ Q 10 2

♠ —
♡ K Q J 10 9 8
◇ 7 3 2
♣ A 8 7 4
Paris

"Paris didn't know it, of course, but both Hera and Athena had opened three spades, been doubled, and had gone for 1100. But this time, just as Paris was pulling out his cards, Aphrodite's gown slipped, and her full moonlit glory was revealed. Dazzled by the vision of Beauty so unexpectedly revealed, the eyes of Paris flickered from his hand to her chest, then back again. 'Two bre—, I mean hearts,' he bid, weakly.

"Immediate protests from Hera and Athena. Bid out of turn. Penalty demanded. Paris to bid what he liked, but his partner to pass throughout. The contract thus remained at two hearts.

"Well, as you can see, there's nothing to the play. Hera and Athena took what they could, but Paris made five hearts, the ace and king of clubs, and was able to ditch one loser on the ace of spades. Plus 110. And, of course, when the scores were compared this board turned out to be the decider, and in his inimitable way Paris delivered his judgemental, er, ditty:

> I love her in her evening gown,
> I love her in her nightie;
> But when moonlight fl—, I mean, rests
> Upon her breasts,
> My choice is Aphrodite.

"There's not much more to tell. Sure, there's a story doing the rounds – and it ties in with what we know of Paris – that the whole thing was a jack-up, with Aphrodite doing a deal beforehand and Paris skimping on the poppies before the final session. Whatever the truth, Hera and Athena were much aggrieved, and Paris may yet live to feel their wrath. But Aphrodite was delighted, and as a reward offered Paris Topless Helen – of all mortals, the one whose physical assets most obviously matched her own. And that is why," Odysseus concluded adamantly, reaching for another apple, "Paris grabbed the next boat to Sparta, leaving poor Oenone weeping in her cave and his sheep dragging their tails behind them, finessed poor old Menelaus, and doubled back to Troy. Truly, when the gods fall out, mortals fall in. We are but rags and pip-cards, to be played at their pleasure, to be trumped at their will. It's a fearsome thought."

[20]

tip. It didn't make sense. Nor did Tiresias, coming over to complain that they hadn't let him finish his story: "'Then do it by logs,' said Zeus triumphantly," said Tiresias triumphantly, but when I too looked at him blankly he stumped off to the cask in the kitchen, muttering something about innumerate nincompoops and saws for wooden heads. But even I, slumped into the corner to ward off Cassandra's advances and criticisms of my drinking ("I told you so!"), felt the change in atmosphere when Paris, whose manners are matched only by his finger-nails, mockingly asked what separates the men from the boys in the Greek camp. We all knew the answer, but only the worm-like Thersites dared speak its name: "A crowbar!" Achilles took the insult personally, made a tasteless comment about the Trojan who woke up with a mouthful of feathers, and would have flattened Paris had not an embarrassed Patroclus held him back. But the damage was done, and for a moment it looked as if things might get ugly.

Protesilaus saved the day. Barging right up to Hector, he challenged the mighty hero to set him a problem, offering to solve it in the standard ten minutes or to be forever shamed. Hector looked at him insolently, and with a dubious "How's your timing?" invited him to make four spades on a heart lead with the following distribution:

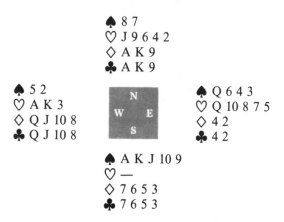

Protesilaus quickly established that nothing was breaking 3–3, and that because East had the queen of spades it would be no use trying to ruff the fourth club or diamond (East would over-ruff, and return a trump); hence, he decided, it would have to be a squeeze; and within a minute he had isolated the following position:

```
        ♠ —
        ♡ —
        ◇ K 9
        ♣ K 9
♠ —                      ♠ —
♡ —        N             ♡ Q 8 7
◇ Q J   W     E          ◇ 4
♣ Q J        S           ♣ —
        ♠ J
        ♡ —
        ◇ 7 6
        ♣ 7
```

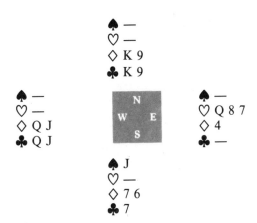

"And," he concluded, "on the last lead of the trump West is simply squeezed. All we've got to do is create that kind of position. So," he paused for thought, "I would ruff the heart; club to the ace; take the spade finesse; diamond to the ace; repeat the finesse; then. . ." His voice tailed off as he realised that East would be under no pressure. "No," he back-tracked. "Let's start again, as Deucalion would say. On the ace of hearts I throw a small diamond; on the king of hearts a small club; on the third heart, another small something. That rectifies the count. If they come back another heart, then I ruff, and the jack in dummy is my tenth trick; and if they switch to either minor then I win in dummy; finesse the spade; return to dummy via the other minor; repeat the finesse, and Bingo, as the plebs say – when I've cashed the two top trumps I've got the position. Where's the problem?"

"Verrry good," purred Hector. "And now, for all drachmas in the jar, tell me how you'd handle a switch to the queen of either minor at trick two. And if you let it hold, to the other queen. And then, if necessary, the heart continuation. You've got five minutes."

Protesilaus agonised at length, but no matter how he tried to rectify the count to prepare for the position there were simply not enough entries to dummy to allow it to be done without losing another trick. So he tried instead to endplay East in hearts, but that line too was easily foiled. With time running out he went over to the cask for fresh inspiration, but it was equally void. In careless contempt Hector threw over the key to the cellar, and told Protesilaus to bring up the next numbered cask ("Though I'd avoid the one marked *K 9 P*," he advised); adding casually that he could have as long on the hand as it took to roll out the barrel.

In humiliation and shame Protesilaus caught the key, marched off to the cellar, and before anyone was aware of what was happening he had locked himself inside, refusing to come out until he had solved the problem. In vain did Hector curse himself for having extended the time limit indefinitely; and in vain did we curse Hector for having handed over the only key to the cellar. And in vain did great Ajax throw his weight against the door, threatening to break every bone in his (Protesilaus's) body. There he was, and there he would stay, not coming out until ten tricks had.

Nobody knew what to do. We sent for Hephaestus, but it would be some time before he could hobble along; and meanwhile our draughts were dwindling. Agamemnon also tried to throw his weight around, ordering Protesilaus out; but our hero remained as unmovable as the door, protesting that both his honour and that of our nation was at stake ("And so will he be, if he doesn't change his mind," muttered Agamemnon furiously). In desperation we finally sent for Laodamia, who was back with the rest of the camp followers ("And she's not the only one *hors de combat*," swore Odysseus grimly. "If we don't get some more wine there won't be much action round here.")

A gloomy silence settled over the hall as we waited for Laodamia to come. Eventually she did, but Protesilaus would open the door only to her, and she too disappeared within. Nothing else happened, and we finally gave up in disgust, heading back to the camp and leaving them to their fate. Only the next day did we hear what happened: it had taken Hephaestus three hours to forge another key; and when the Trojans finally descended the winding stairway, their tempers flaming like their torches, it was to find the two of them lying amidst the debris, as dead to the world as the empty flasks around them. And there, inscribed in candle grease upon the mildewed wall, was the following message:

Dummy Reversal, Dummy. Ruff ♡, *A* ♣, *Ruff* ♡, *A* ♢, *R* ♡, *K* ♣, *R* ♡, *K* ♢, *R* ♡ = 9 tricks, and *8 7* ♠ = 10. Hector is a Horse's Uncle.*

"That's as may be," observed Odysseus sagely, when the news was relayed to us. "But with Agamemnon as mad as a March Hatter I don't fancy the chances of Protesilaus. Still, that's at least one headache lifted from our shoulders if he's sent off; and it's an ill wind that cools no porridge, as they say – who knows, getting the Trojans mad like that may even help us in the long turn. But I'd say that the early worm got caught, and it looks like first blood to the Trojans."

[25]

V

The Trojan Fork

Note: After Paris had stolen Helen, but long before the fighting
began, the Greeks tried to avert a lengthy combat by sending
an embassy to Troy, demanding the return of both Helen and
the riches filched by Paris when he had abducted her.
Menelaus and Odysseus were chosen as ambassadors. They
made their way to Troy, where they were hospitably received
by Antenor, son of Priam; but despite the latter's urgings and
Cassandra's prophecies of doom Paris and the Trojans were
unwilling to relinquish Helen, and the two Greeks were forced
to return home empty-handed. Odysseus, smarting at the set-
back, later explained to a few of us why the negotiations had
reached such a sudden parting of the ways. . .

"There are tides in the affairs of men," Odysseus began, somewhat
sententiously, "that leave you stranded no matter what you do. There
are cross-roads in life where you are doomed to meet your destiny –
Oedipus can tell you all about them. And there are hands in bridge
that are perversely fated – where all leads roam to Rhodes, as they
say."

His words were defensive, and small wonder, for the mission had
been a total failure. With the angelic Menelaus as our messenger some
of us hadn't expected any better, but Odysseus was taking it very
badly. "Doomed from the start," he kept muttering, "doomed from
the start."

Travelling expenses were at the heart of it: we had just been told
that to get them we were expected to stay long after everything was
over, by which time our contracts with our rowers would have long
expired, and would have to be re-negotiated. Rule XXII, they called
it. We had wanted greater flexibility, a rescheduling of events, but
(following the Protesilaus affair) the Trojans had become increasingly
bloody-minded and had ignored our just request. We had therefore
resolved to send a deputation to them, and Menelaus, entitled to the
family rebate if he could win back Helen, was determined to be part
of it. Some of us were hesitant about that, as Menelaus of the loud
war-cry has a habit of opening his mouth and changing feet; but we
figured that if Odysseus went with him then all might not be lost.

Odysseus, mean as custard, wasn't particularly enthused, but allowed himself to be persuaded when Agamemnon promised that he could shoot home early. So the two of them had made their way to tall-gated Troy, only to return much later with empty hands and frowning scowls. All we had been told was that they'd been asked to prove their credentials in play, and with the best players in Troy still involved with the Trials they'd been relegated to the side-game. If they did well there, Antenor had said, their request might be considered. They had not done well, but until Odysseus took up the tale we were unaware just how badly things had gone.

"I don't want to be unfair," he continued, "but Zeus preserve the poor creature who has to put up with Menelaus when the tournament proper begins. He's not completely hopeless, I suppose, but he still thinks Stayman's part of a flower and Flint's for lighting fires. And given any kind of an option he seems to have a psychological compulsion to make the wrong choice." We nodded in agreement, for the assessment was not unjust. Menelaus often leads a charmed life, gaining by thud and blunder what others achieve by finesse. But every now and then the law of averages catches up on him – though if recent events were anything to go by, he should be all right for the next ten years.

It turned out that they had come absolutely bottom in a very weak field – the carrot-patch, it was called – and as a result had been hooted out of Troy. Rightly or wrongly, though, Odysseus felt there was more to it than bad play, that the gods in fact had intervened to make rueful rabbits of them both, thereby aggravating the bad feeling that already existed.

"We began badly," he went on, "and we finished worse, but some things were quite inexplicable. We were playing basic Attic, with nothing fancy, and I suppose we should have known that an opening hand opposite an opening hand means one down – but why were we the only ones doubled? And when Menelaus bids clubs he should have clubs, the way the gods intend – none of that fancy Delphic nonsense here." After the first couple of disasters he had tried to console Menelaus with the sentiment that many hands make a tall horse, but Menelaus was still depressed, and the next board flattened him completely. They were up against Helen and Cassandra, and if there was ever a chance to get something back, this was surely it. Apparently Helen hadn't believed Cassandra's bidding on the two previous hands, and they were already glaring at each other. But this time Helen had the points, and the bidding too was short and sweet:

$$2\clubsuit \quad \ldots \quad 2\diamondsuit$$
$$6\clubsuit$$

Menelaus, sitting over Helen with ♠ K J 7, ♡ 5 4, ◊ A 7 6 4 2, ♣ Q 8 6, couldn't resist the double, and was then faced with the choice of lead. Not a spade, obviously, nor a club (the gods are powerless against the stupidity of men), and a heart might well give away a free finesse. Besides, he could remember only too well that ominous time when his failure to cash the ace of diamonds had led to total disaster. The ace of diamonds it therefore had to be! The ace of diamonds it was:

Board 13
All Vulnerable

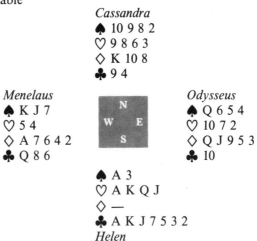

Cassandra
♠ 10 9 8 2
♡ 9 8 6 3
◊ K 10 8
♣ 9 4

Menelaus
♠ K J 7
♡ 5 4
◊ A 7 6 4 2
♣ Q 8 6

Odysseus
♠ Q 6 5 4
♡ 10 7 2
◊ Q J 9 5 3
♣ 10

♠ A 3
♡ A K Q J
◊ —
♣ A K J 7 5 3 2
Helen

As she laid down her dummy Cassandra muttered something about hearts being better, but nobody took any notice. And even when his ace was ruffed Menelaus didn't look too worried – dummy was as dead as Daphne, and Helen was destined to lose all by playing from her hand. Down came the jack of clubs!!

Odysseus took up the tale again. "With the clarity of Tiresias, Menelaus suddenly saw himself as the plaything of the gods: the jack would pin my ten, but if he took the queen then the 9 of clubs would be an entry to the king of diamonds to pitch a loser; while if he ducked there would be no losing club. A perfect example of the Trojan Fork – unlike the Greek Gift, if you refuse the offering you're just as badly off. His fate was certain, but Menelaus ducked the jack (knowing that if he didn't then I would have the singleton king, and the gods and Trojans the last laugh). Six clubs, doubled, making six.

"And what made it worse was that as she filled in the score Helen confessed to Cassandra that she thought she'd played the ace, and couldn't believe it when we didn't take the trick ('I had a losing spade,' she said, looking scornfully at poor Menelaus). Don't know what he and Paris see in her, myself.

"It obviously wasn't going to matter what we did from that point on," he concluded. "The gods had had their fun, and bitter strife was now a certainty. And as we left the table, with me muttering Oedipal cross words about partners who lead aces against slams, it was then that I heard the voice of Apollo, calling like a cuckoo from the gloom: 'Smile, and be happy! Things could be worse.' So I smiled, and was happy, and Lo!" He paused dramatically. "Things did get worse."

VI

Chryseis Retains her Honour

Note: The Greeks, though at first unsuccessful against Troy, had taken a number of neighbouring towns and allied cities, and in the division of the spoils a female captive by the name of Chryseis had fallen to the lot of Agamemnon. Her father Chryses, a priest of Apollo, came to Agamemnon bearing the sacred emblems of his office and begging the release of his daughter. Agamemnon refused, whereupon Chryses implored Apollo to afflict the Greeks until their commander should release his captive. Apollo heard the prayer, and sent pestilence into the Greek camp; and Achilles, at a special council, charged Agamemnon with the responsibility for the misfortune. In great rage Agamemnon agreed to relinquish his captive, but demanded instead that the Greeks should yield to him Briseis, who had fallen to Achilles in the distribution of the plunder. Achilles submitted, but declaring that he would take no further part in the war withdrew into his tent. That decision was greatly to affect the subsequent events of the war, but, those involved being no better than they ought to be, it is difficult to imagine a more honourable resolution. . .

They say it's all the fault of Apollo, but I'm not so sure. Agamemnon and Achilles should have been able to sort things out better, and Chryseis of the icy countenance has got a bit to answer for. It all goes back to the early days when we were setting up camp, and needed a couple of wenches to warm the supper and make the beds, or vice versa. Calchas, our soothsayer, went off to sort out applicants from one of the nearby towns, and came back with a couple of sweet young things called Briseis and Chryseis. But when we asked him how he had got on – trying out the cooking, the cleaning, etc – he was a bit evasive: "Well, yes and no," was all he'd say. Seems that as far as the old vice versa was concerned, the one was chaste and the other all too easily caught: Briseis was game for anything, but Chryseis was cold – told him he was confusing her with that Trojan trollop Cresseid, and said she wasn't remotely interested in making a prophet. Seems that she's waiting to be a Vestal Virgin, and doesn't want to disqualify herself from contention just yet.

Anyway, Agamemnon was quite enthralled by the ice-maiden, and Achilles more than happy with Briseis, so the deal was quickly done. And for a while all seemed in order – happy squeals from Achilles's tent, a cool refreshing silence from Agamemnon's. And with our domestic affairs under control we were able at last to plan our tactics, sharpen our little pencils, and polish up our bidding for the tournament which was about to begin.

Then who should turn up but old Chryses, father of Chryseis, decked out in all his finery. Coming, he proclaimed, from the Temple of Apollo, where a vacancy for Vestal Virgin had just turned up – one of the previous priestesses, it seems, having slipped from her pedestal somewhat (the old "candle her Nemesis/Parthenogenesis" problem, presumably). Chryseis was to present herself before the sacred flame; and when she heard the summons she pronounced herself ready.

Agamemnon, however, wasn't having any of that kind of nonsense. He rudely told Chryses to go and get trumped, and informed Chryseis that she would be staying with us. Chryses, in the mildest of threatening tones, warned him against offending Apollo; while Achilles, always a bit superstitious, also asked if he would reconsider, and was in turn told where to go and how to do it. And as he was bundled off the premises Chryses lost his cool a little – "A plague on both your tents," he shouted – and said he'd be back in a couple of days to see if we'd changed our minds.

Well, that was the beginning of the disaster, and from that moment on everything went wrong for us – finesses failing, trumps breaking 5–0, critical cards in the wrong hands. Our scores were plummeting to the low thirties when Chryses returned, and by then even Agamemnon was starting to appreciate the seriousness of the situation.

He still wasn't entirely penitent, though. He insisted to Chryses that Chryseis was his by right of contract, if not conquest, and even talked about taking her back to Mycenae when the tournament was over. And when Chryses suggested that the Oracle should decide matters once and for all, he agreed, but held out for the further condition that should he prevail then Chryseis should be his in every way – intense Platonic love not altogether the ideal, we gathered.

Chryses had no objection, nor did Chryseis – Platonic love in tents not altogether the ideal, we gathered. So the sacrificial oxen were slaughtered, and the conditions of contest decreed. One hand would suffice, the Oracle announced, for thereby the will of Apollo would be revealed. Agamemnon and Achilles were to sit North–South, and their future destinies would be foreshadowed in the play of the hand:

[31]

Agamemnon
♠ A J
♡ K 10 9
♦ A K J 4 2
♣ Q J 7

Chryseis
♠ K Q 9 4
♡ A 5 3
♦ Q 9 5
♣ K 6 5

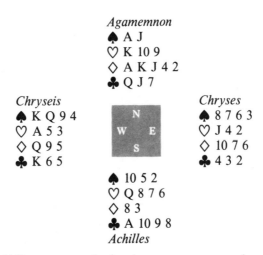

Chryses
♠ 8 7 6 3
♡ J 4 2
♦ 10 7 6
♣ 4 3 2

♠ 10 5 2
♡ Q 8 7 6
♦ 8 3
♣ A 10 9 8
Achilles

The bidding was emphatic: Agamemnon opened an Offensive Club, but Achilles bid the no trumps first, and, to Agamemnon's mixed feelings of chagrin and relief, was left to play in three. Chryseis led the king of spades, which Achilles won in dummy; and the Queen of clubs was run successfully, Chryses dropping the 4, and Chryseis the 6. Achilles now ran the jack of clubs, both father and daughter completing their echoes. Achilles hesitated, but not for long. If he were to cash the ace of clubs and find the diamond finesse wrong he could lose five tricks, and everything pointed to the clubs behaving. He therefore repeated the finesse, and Chryseis won with her bare honour. She then found the perfect ploy: back came the 9 of spades, which Achilles was forced to win in dummy, leaving this position:

♠ —
♡ K 10 9
♦ A K J 4 2
♣ —

♠ Q 4
♡ A 5 3
♦ Q 9 5
♣ —

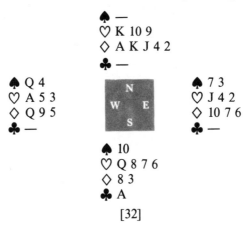

♠ 7 3
♡ J 4 2
♦ 10 7 6
♣ —

♠ 10
♡ Q 8 7 6
♦ 8 3
♣ A

[32]

No matter what he did, Achilles now had to lose four more tricks. His own hand was dead, and however he played the heart suit Chryseis could make him lose two hearts or force him to lead from the A–K–J of diamonds: if he played the king of hearts, she would hold off; and if he tried at any point to run the 9 or 10 then Chryses would cover with the jack, and the defenders would either win two heart tricks or put Achilles back on the table.

The final diagnosis was crystal-clear: with ten tricks there for the taking on the correct play of the diamonds Achilles and Agamemnon were transparently the goats, and Chryseis was thus saved from a fate worse than a finesse. Agamemnon, however, was most cut up about it. He turned on Achilles in fury, blaming him entirely for the disaster, and insisted that he give up Briseis in compensation. Achilles, of course, was highly indignant and his pride deeply wounded. However for once the gods were not on the side of the big biceps, and he was forced to surrender his prize, declaring, however, that that was his first and last hand of the tournament, and that he'd be going back to bed until his ships were ready to depart.

"Talk about crises," declared Odysseus afterwards, as we sat round munching sacrificial oxen. "We're in big trouble, I'm afraid. Achilles is obviously going to take this lying down, and Agamemnon won't mind in the least now that he's got Briseis to play with. Apollo's obviously got it in for us for insulting his acolytes, and it's going to take some time to make amends. Still, you've got to hand it to Chryseis – that contract was equally frigid, and in the circumstances it took some doing to hold on to her honour. It's what you might call a perfect example of immaculate defence."

VII

The Spartan Redouble

Note: The opposing forces were arrayed before Troy, and were about
to clash when Paris stepped forward and offered single combat
to any Argive champion. Menelaus, grievously wronged by
Paris, accepted the challenge so vigorously that Paris quailed;
but Hector roused him from his couch and urged that the duel
should take place, the winner to claim Helen as his wife. Before
the walls of Troy, with Helen and Priam looking on, the
combat began. Paris attacked first, but was easily repulsed;
then Menelaus retaliated, breaking his spear and sword
against Paris. Undeterred, Menelaus seized his adversary by
the strap of his helmet, and things would have gone hard for
Paris had Aphrodite not intervened to save her champion.
Menelaus was thus deemed the victor, but the fact that he did
not immediately win back Helen, allied with what we already
know of the real Menelaus, suggests that the truth was perhaps
a little different than the popular account would have it. . .

When Agamemnon posted the pairings, I couldn't believe my eyes.
Here was I, the valiant Diomedes, wounder of the gods, friend of
Odysseus and backbone of the fighting Greeks, set down to play with
spineless Menelaus! Menelaus! The so-called King of Sparta! That
red-haired buffoon who couldn't stop Paris finessing his Queen,
which had caused all the trouble in the first place. There'd be no
laurels for me out of this lot!

Furious, I dashed into Agamemnon's tent and loudly demanded
justice, only to be told that if the Greeks were to inherit the earth then
it was up to me to dig in and do my bit, and that if I didn't like it I'd
quickly find myself first volunteer for the Wooden Bunny. Silly old
fool! Serve him right if Clytemnestra carves him up for coming home
late.

The trouble with Menelaus is simply that he's not very brave. Not
one of the Hot Gates Band, by any stretch of the imagination. More
the Gerontion type, one of the Brown Trow Brigade. The word
'vulnerable' makes him wish he were home in his wind-swept halls,
while 'double' fair makes his shiver in his sandals ('REDOUBLE'
doesn't bear thinking about). It was obviously up to me to push some

[34]

stuffing into him – not an easy task. But I said to him, I said, "Now, Menelaus, it's up to us to show 'em. If you 'aven't got 'em, pretend you 'ave. Psyche 'em out, and we'll be 'Eros."

Well, it didn't start too badly. The first few skirmishes we did all right, holding our own (as the Vestal Virgin said to the tragedian). Then I noticed rosy-fingered M turn a whiter shade of pale, and following his gaze I saw that Paris and Hector, mightiest of Troy, were next in line. Worse, they were being kibitzed by Helen and Priam, obviously waiting for Menelaus to make a bigger fool of himself. The barest civilities were exchanged, and battle began:

Hector
♠ K 9 4 2
♡ A J 9 8 7
♢ J
♣ A Q 6

Menelaus
♠ A Q 8 3
♡ Q 5 3 2
♢ Q 10 9 3
♣ 2

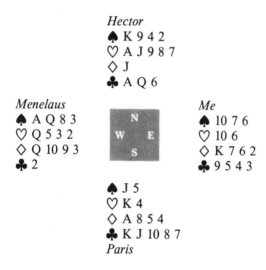

Me
♠ 10 7 6
♡ 10 6
♢ K 7 6 2
♣ 9 5 4 3

♠ J 5
♡ K 4
♢ A 8 5 4
♣ K J 10 8 7
Paris

Sitting East, red against white, I took one look at my collection of chariot tickets, and decided against taking any further part in the action. The Trojans had grafted our Delphic Diamond onto their Belligerent Club, so Paris hit off with one ambiguous diamond. To my horror, there was a faint squeak from Menelaus, *ridiculus mus*, which, translated, apparently meant 'double'. The loud and immediate 'REDOUBLE' from Hector guaranteed a hecatomb or two, but having no suit and even fewer hopes I passed, as did Paris, as did Menelaus. He was later to call it a Positive Pass (with 10 points opposite 3??), a gods-inspired polishing of the Shining Hour, a lightning-like Analysis; but I saw the flicker in his eyes as he too saw himself carried home upon his shield.

The sparring was fast and furious. The feeblest of clubs was flourished, and battered by the ace. Then the jack of diamonds was led to its ace; and was followed by another diamond, Menelaus winning the 9. The ace of spades was now cashed; then the queen was played, inadvertently pinning the jack (with every small card exposed like Spartan weaklings, Menelaus had nevertheless read my 6 as encouraging). The king of spades won in dummy; a third spade was ruffed in hand; a club led to the table, the queen winning (Menelaus conserving his trumps, he later claimed – ha!). Then came a heart to the king; and another one back to the jack (another chic Parisian finesse!).The ace of hearts was then led from table. Conscious only that the REDOUBLED contract had been made, and still benumbed by my partner's pass, I ruffed in with the 7 of trumps rather than the king, and thereby permitted Paris to score his miserable 8 for an overtrick. One diamond, REDOUBLED, making two!

We sat in abject dejection as the triumphant Trojans unwrapped the travelling vellum, only to stare in total disbelief at what the Fates had decreed. Plus 380 was like the dingy bottom of Tartarus for the haughty heroes of Troy, for even the minor mercenaries and drunken Helots had managed 400 or more!

Erat Hora, indeed! The most high gods could not have asked any better thing than one such sunlit hour! An atrocious double, a ferocious REDOUBLE, and totally unheroic and abject misdefence (the latter described, in unnecessary detail, by Menelaus around the camp-fire later that night). The gods indeed bestow their garland in strange ways upon the least deserving of mortals! And as we proceeded to greater glory, the words of the Hebrew prophet Ezra pounded through my mind:

> O bright Apollo,
> τίν' ἄνδρα, τίν' ἥρωα, τίνα θεόν,
> What god, man, or hero
> Shall I place a tin wreath upon!

VIII

The Achilles Heel (I)

Note: When the Greeks were assembling their forces for Troy, they wished to recruit Achilles. Thetis, mother of Achilles, knowing that her son was fated to perish if he went to Troy (despite having been made almost invulnerable as an infant, by being dipped into the River Styx), tried to prevent his going by disguising him as a woman and hiding him at the court of Scyros. Odysseus, disguised as a merchant, visited the court where Achilles was hidden, and offered for sale female ornaments, amongst which he had placed some arms; and while the women played with the trinkets, Achilles revealed himself by choosing the weapons. He was persuaded to go to Troy, but in the early days of the fighting refused to take part because Agamemnon had taken from him the Trojan woman Briseis, who had fallen to Achilles's lot. But Odysseus was again prevailed upon to tell the real version of the story. . .

We were sitting around the camp-fire between sessions, quaffing the odd mead or three, when the conversation got round to Achilles, who was still sulking in his tent and still hadn't turned out to play. "Why on earth was he chosen to play in the first place?" asked young Aias, who had only just arrived. "And why won't he play? He's acting like a big girl."

"Ah," said Odysseus. "Thereby hangs a tail. To take your questions one by one: he was chosen because on form he's the best player we've got. Or perhaps," he qualified it modestly, "the second best. And he won't play because Agamemnon won't let him partner Briseis, the Trojan girl who warms our supper. And if he's acting like

[37]

a big girl, that's quite in keeping with the way he got into the team in the first place." He reached for the amphora, and we settled back comfortably, knowing we were fated to hear yet another of his inconclusive experiences.

"It all goes back to Thetis," he began. "She of the shining breasts. Achilles's old lady. For all that she's a demi-goddess, she's no great shakes at playing the hand. And about the time that the trials were held to pick the Open team for Troy, the women were also picking their team for the match against the Amazons. Thetis knew she didn't have a god's show of getting in without a decent partner, and who better than Achilles? So, with a bit of help from Aphrodite (who didn't want him to go either), she had her son tarted up as a daughter, and entered the two of them for the women's trials."

"But what was his/her name?" asked young Aias. "And why did nobody recognise him?"

"Puzzling questions, indeed," admitted Odysseus. "Like what song the Sirens sing – remind me to check that out on the way home. Let's say it was Sue – with a name like that he'd be bound to end up as a professional."

"Or a law-maker," interrupted Palamedes, drily.

"And why couldn't he be recognised?" continued Odysseus, ignoring the interruption (he can't stand Palamedes). "That's where it's useful being a demi-goddess. Even if you can't influence the cards dealt by Fate, you can still cast the kind of spell over ordinary mortals that prevents them seeing things as they really are. Right, Tiresias?"

"Right," grunted Tiresias. "When it came to the trials, and you wanted to know which one was Achilles, I couldn't help at all. Even his wise father wouldn't have known him. All I could discern was that he'd be sitting South."

"Well," Odysseus went on, "that was enough as it turned out. We had to get him out and into the Open team – Zeus only knows how much we need him. And if we could expose him – figuratively, that is – as a man, the Amazons would make such a fuss that we'd be bound to get him. Look at the way they objected to Tiresias, even after he'd had his sex-change. So we needed a hand, to be played by South, through which Achilles would draw attention to himself. I was Director for the women's trials, and I set this hand up in advance." He passed round the papyrus:

Board 13
All Vulnerable

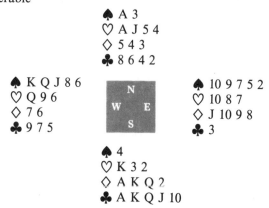

                          ♠ A 3
                          ♡ A J 5 4
                          ◇ 5 4 3
                          ♣ 8 6 4 2

    ♠ K Q J 8 6   ♠ 10 9 7 5 2
    ♡ Q 9 6   N   ♡ 10 8 7
    ◇ 7 6   W   E   ◇ J 10 9 8
    ♣ 9 7 5   S   ♣ 3

                          ♠ 4
                          ♡ K 3 2
                          ◇ A K Q 2
                          ♣ A K Q J 10

"I don't get it," said young Aias, puzzled. "Sure, six clubs or six no trumps are a piece of pi on the heart finesse, and seven on the 3–3 split, but even Achilles wouldn't bid seven. And everybody else would surely bid six."

"Exactly," chuckled Odysseus. "Mind you, I needed a little help from Hera, who can't stand Thetis, to make sure that every South would bid the slam in no trumps rather than clubs – those extra match-points, you know – otherwise it wouldn't have worked. And, of course, they made it. All but one. Every score was plus 1470, except Achilles who was minus 100."

Nobody got it, so Odysseus explained. "Achilles, as you know, is our best, or rather, our second best player. Totally immune from revokes, unnecessary ruffs and minor stupidities – something to do with having been dunked in the River Plate as a child. But he has one fatal weakness – squeezes. Like what's-his-name in Egypt, he would lose all the world for a squeeze, and be content to lose it. Given the choice of making a slam on a simple finesse or a squeeze, he'll take the squeeze every time. As you can see, thirteen tricks are there on the heart finesse, and everybody else took them. There's no point in holding up in spades if you're going to have to finesse anyway, so everybody made seven. But I knew Achilles would dismiss the chance of finding hearts 3–3 with the queen onside, and would play for the squeeze. It's a reasonable shot, for if either defender has the queen of hearts and four diamonds he, sorry, she's going to be helpless against the run of the clubs. So Achilles held off the king of spades to rectify

[39]

the count. He won the spade continuation, discarding a heart from hand, then played off one diamond and five rounds of clubs. West threw a diamond and a spade, North tossed away a heart, while East on the last club squirmed a little (or did Achilles imagine it?) before letting go a heart. The position, in Achilles's mind, was quite clear:

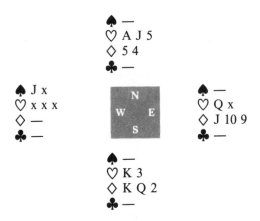

Having ducked the first trick, putting himself a trick behind the rest of the room, Achilles was committed to playing the king of hearts and then the ace, expecting the queen to drop. When it didn't he had to concede a diamond. Our man was marked. At the end of the play I had Ganymede bring Thetis a spiked libation, and the moment she was under the table we dragged Achilles away from it. Of course," he added ruefully, "we had to promise him Briseis, and hence all the trouble with Agamemnon, who hadn't been told that part of the plan and wants to play with her himself."

"Don't blame him," came the chorus of voices from out of the darkness.

"And that is why," Odysseus concluded, "Achilles is sitting in his tent and playing with himself while we sink deeper into the brown Augean. It's all the fault of that Trojan trollop. As the Amazons might thay in their breath-less way, a man needs a woman like Pegasus needs a fish. We've got to get Achilles to stop being a big dummy, and get him going again. It's going to take some affirmative action, but that's another problem."

IX

Ajax Finds a Duck

Note: The Greek forces, sorely pressed, were beset by the Trojans
who had succeeded in forcing their way through the ramparts
and were about to fire the ships, when Poseidon, seeing the
Greeks in such peril, appeared to them and raised their ardour
to such a pitch that they were able to force the enemy back.
Ajax, in particular, performed prodigies of valour, and
eventually encountered Hector, who threw his lance at the
valiant Greek. Ajax withstood the blow, and then retaliated by
seizing a huge stone and throwing it at Hector, who, failing to
duck, was stretched out upon the dusty plain and borne off,
stunned and wounded. But what really aroused the slow-
witted Ajax to such a height of fury was the despicable fowl
play of the Trojans. . .

He had always been the solitary type, Ajax. Not the brightest, mind
you – strong as an ox, Thersites would say, and almost as clever. And
Agamemnon had once been heard in a training session praying to
Archimedes for a big enough lever to turn him round at half time. But
he would consistently plod his way to 55%, following suit and taking
his tricks before they got away, and never outsmarting himself. So
when the team was chosen, he and young Aias had been an automatic
selection.

And in the early days at Troy he did well enough, even when the rest
of us had our backs to the ships. After a while, though, we noticed
that he was behaving just a bit oddly. Nothing very obvious – after all,
we all live in our little Ptolemaic universes – but trivial things such as
holding his cards upside down, playing inverted minors, and insisting
on reverse signals and discards. But still getting 55%. We had a word
with the quack, who thought he might be missing the missus, but to
those of us who'd been to Salamis that seemed unlikely – his old
harpie would drive anybody clean round the bend, and Ajax had
seemed quite relieved at the thought of getting away from her for a
while.

Yet he was obviously lonely, and whoreson Thersites didn't help
very much, jeering at his slow play, and generally giving him a hard
time. "Stand closer," he would say when they met in the Jakes. "It

may be shorter than you think." But Ajax, instead of daubing the wall with him, would stolidly go about his business, and then when play had finished would head off on long solitary walks along the shore. One day he came back from his ramble, his big hands tenderly cupped around an ugly little duckling which he had found, he said, in a trampled nest on the banks of the Scamander River, and which he was going to look after. We stared in disbelief as mighty Ajax, bulwark of the Achaeans, took the bird back to his tent and built her a little nest amidst his loot. Quite daffy, we thought.

Time passed, and the little creature grew quite big. Ajax nursed her through the pip, the roup, and the gapes, sharing his rations with her, until she was plump and healthy. Daphne, he decided to call her, and the two of them were virtually inseparable. And when she laid her first egg, he was as pleased as any new father. In truth, we were getting rather fond of her too. All except scaly-legged Thersites. He would stand in front of Ajax, salute ironically, and say, "Take me to your Leda." And when bumblefooted Ajax didn't get it, he'd try the other old one about Zeus and the swan, and ask Ajax the difference between erotic sex and perverted sex. Ajax fell for it, of course, and on being told that erotic sex used a feather but perverted sex the whole duck, he'd let out a bellow of rage and chase Thersites right through the camp.

The trouble began when Ajax decided to take Daphne with him into action, the duck nestling on his shoulder. The Trojans protested, of course, but Ajax of the mighty biceps pointed out that there was nothing in the rules specifically to prohibit it, that Achilles had his tortoise and Paris and Hector their blue bunny, that he was the one who had to wash his tunics, and that who was going to stop him anyway? He was too big to argue with, so Daphne came for the ride, and with her upon his shoulder Ajax seemed much happier, and his scores gradually crept up to the 60% mark.

The tragedy occurred one winter's day, at the end of the afternoon session, when Ajax left Daphne behind at the table while he went off to get the libations. When he came back she had gone, and a distraught Aias told him how Paris, true to form, had seized her and raced back to the Trojan lines. Ajax could barely be restrained from charging the walls on his own when he heard this, but we held him back, telling him that it was a joke (albeit a dirty one), and that she'd be back that evening. And we hoped he wouldn't notice the smell of roasting fat that wafted towards our camp a little later.

The unsavoury Paris rubbed in the salt when the Trojans returned.

[42]

"I say, Hector," he called out, in the hearing of Ajax, "should one or should one not eat duck with the fingers?" "Only cooked duck," Hector gravely replied. It was, we agreed, a paltry trick, and we looked with some concern at great Ajax, who stood there as solid as a rock, and said nothing.

Ajax was in devastating form that night, a real white tornado: cleaning up opponents, wiping out honours, finding squeezes and other sparkling plays. His score was close to 72% when he and Aias reached the final table, where Paris and Hector were awaiting their arrival in some trepidation. But Ajax was impassive, and there were no ritual greetings as the hand got under way:

Paris
♠ 4 2
♡ 9 7
◇ A J 10 6 5 2
♣ Q 8 3

Aias
♠ Q 10 9 7
♡ Q 10 5 2
◇ 7 3
♣ 6 5 2

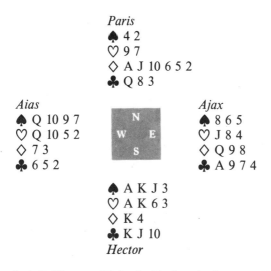

Ajax
♠ 8 6 5
♡ J 8 4
◇ Q 9 8
♣ A 9 7 4

♠ A K J 3
♡ A K 6 3
◇ K 4
♣ K J 10
Hector

Playing their Belligerent Club, the Trojans had no trouble bashing their way to three no trumps, and Aias did well to lead a heart rather than a spade. Hector did his best by putting in the 9, but Ajax covered with the jack, forcing the king. And at that moment Ajax made the key play – and to this very day we don't know if it was sublime or ridiculous – of inverting his cards in such a way that Hector could see his entire hand, including the queen of diamonds. Hector also saw the chance of glory, a way of getting a top despite the unfavourable lead. He carelessly played his 4 of diamonds to dummy's jack, planning on overtaking his king with dummy's ace later, and thereby making at least ten tricks. But to his surprise Ajax found the duck, and Hector was now as dead as Daphne.

Knowing that the spade finesse was destined to lose, he did his best to survive by trying to knock out the ace of clubs, but Ajax held off twice; so Hector cashed his king of diamonds before exiting with the last club. Ajax took his ace and cashed the 9 (Hector and Aias discarding spades); but didn't make the mistake of exiting with a heart, choosing instead a spade. Hector went up with the ace, and tried to end-play Aias in hearts by cashing the king and another; but Aias (having unblocked the 10) also found the duck, letting Ajax win with the 8; and when another spade shot through Hector was brought down.

It wasn't a complete top for Ajax and Aias, for a few game birds had tried the diamond finesse and also gone down, but it was good enough for 72%, since most were making nine tricks on a spade lead or some kind of end-play. Paris took it badly, being outwitted by Ajax, and when the latter, courteous to a fault, asked him to name his poison from the cellar, he rudely muttered that he'd like some Cold Duck.

It was more than Ajax could take. The nearest object was a stone jug, on a tray carried by Ganymede, and Ajax, seizing it by the handle, swung it at Paris, who was lucky enough to duck in the nick of time. Not so Hector. The jug hit him fair and square, and the doughty Trojan hero was laid out flat upon the dusty floor. A little unwillingly, we restrained Ajax before he could demolish Paris as well, and as both sides carried off their wounded, wise Odysseus sagely reflected. "My, my," he said to me. "That's about it for Ajax, I'm afraid. There's going to have to be a special meeting about that little episode, and they're bound to send him off for a good long spell of R & R. You know what they say about ducks that fly upside down – they quack up. That's the last swing our Ajax will be making for quite a while."

X

Rhesus Seeks Promotion

Note: Despite the mighty efforts of Ajax and others, the Greeks
found themselves severely under pressure, and, unable to
sleep, Menelaus and Agamemnon held council and decided to
send out spies among the Trojans to find out their plans of
attack. Diomedes and Odysseus were chosen for the task. The
formidable pair set out, and encountered on the way the
Trojan spy Dolon, whom they captured and "persuaded" to
talk. Dolon revealed the enemy plans, and, according to one
tradition, told of the prophecy that should the horses of
Rhesus drink from the Scamander River the City of Troy
would be safe forever. Diomedes and Odysseus therefore
resolved, having dispatched Dolon to an untimely death, to
visit the Trojan encampment, steal the horses, and bring them
back to the Greek tents. In this they succeeded, but, as always,
the traditional account and the actual sequence of events are
two different things. . .

Omar's Circus was back in town, and there was to be a special late-
night show; but Agamemnon, wanting us wide awake for the next
day's play, had imposed a curfew. Odysseus and I, however, not
wanting the Trojans to get the jump on us with any new tricks,
decided that we would go anyhow, and that night, when Menelaus
and Agamemnon were sound asleep (in every sense), we sneaked out
between our sentries and made our way over the dusty plain towards
the citadel.

The place was a hive of activity, with torches ablaze about the arena, and the crowds rolling up to the show. Quietly we slipped beneath the canvas, and worked our way to the ringside seats, where we would have the best view of any graphic action. The lime-light flared, the players came out, and the greatest show on earth began.

It was, we later agreed, something of a disappointment. There had been a couple of good things – Ruby, Pride of the Ring, demonstrating her latest strip-squeeze for a big top; and some fine examples of balancing – but there had been too many basic mistakes – strongman Heracles struggling in the wrong suit, for instance; and Icarus getting too high, for a big flop. Odysseus, however, had been quite taken by Trixi the biddable mare – shown thirteen cards she would tap out her bids with her hooves, and by and large did as well as her human or Trojan opponents. Sceptics in the audience thought she might be responding to signals from Rhesus, her master; but when asked if this was so she emphatically spelt out 'N–O', to the satisfaction of all.

So perhaps it had been worth while after all, we decided, making our way through certain half-deserted streets, looking for an insidious restaurant to wash away the taste of sawdust. We were joined there by a Trojan named Dolon, son of Eumedes he informed us, who'd seen us at the show, and, not recognising us as Greeks, wanted to compare notes. Well, talk about talkative! With him as your prisoner there'd be no need to tell the executioner to blunten his instruments. Within a few minutes we'd learnt the Trojan line-up for the morrow, and about how superstitious Rhesus was (believes in Hippogriffs, it seems), and where his tent was located, and how he had another mare called Peggy which could fly (we knew then that he'd been drinking too much) – all this, and so much more. We were half listening, waiting for a chance to make a break, when suddenly our attention was caught by something he'd been saying.

". . . probably be invincible then, Paris and Hector, if Rhesus gets that sponsorship deal going for the game against the greasy Greeks" – we ignored that – "after all, ten drachmas an IMP is quite some incentive. . ."

Odysseus broke in, feigning ignorance to find out more. "Rhesus," he said. "Sounds like the name of a bloody monkey. Where would he get ten drachmas from?" And he put another couple of drinks in front of Dolon, whose words tumbled out faster than a speeding ticket.

It all built up to something quite ominous. Having made his pile in Corn and Whey, the wealthy Rhesus wanted to be appointed non-playing captain of the Trojan team, and was apparently willing to

[46]

make a generous offer of sponsorship to achieve his goal. All Troy was buzzing with the rumour, and I looked at Odysseus with barely concealed dismay, for an incentive like that would surely urge the Trojans on to impossible heights.

We poured Dolon another couple of pain-killers to keep him quiet, and left him there dead to the world. Then we went outside, but instead of heading for our camp Odysseus turned back towards the centre of the town. "We've got work to do," he said, in response to my mute inquiry, "and I think we'd better pay a call at the Temple of Apollo before we go any further." This rather surprised me, as Odysseus does not usually display such piety towards the gods, but I was quickly put into the picture: we were going to "borrow" some priestly robes, a couple of torches, and a two-sided white board, before calling in on Rhesus.

For, Odysseus explained as we made our way to the Temple, Dolon had told us that Rhesus was incurably superstitious – like that fellow who plays the Swiss convention, where you bid what you haven't got, that fellow who wrote the manual on 'Chariots of the Gods' – Rhesus was one of those who attributes to the gods anything he doesn't understand, and, not basically understanding anything at all, therefore sees evidence of the gods everywhere. The plan was to take advantage of such superstition, and convince Rhesus that Apollo did not approve of his scheme.

Thus it was that we made our way to the white tent of Rhesus dressed in the garb of Priests of Apollo, and at the command of Odysseus I flicked my flint to ignite our torches and awaken Rhesus from his dreams of glory. He started from his sleep, and in tones of fear and terror asked us who we were, and what system we represented (he talks like that).

"We are acolytes," Odysseus solemnly informed him. "We have just come from the Temple of Apollo" – that much was true – "to ascertain whether or not thou art worthy of the honour thou seekest in thy promotion. The glories of the gods, and the duties of those who tend them, are not to be taken lightly, nor by those serving first their own ends."

Rhesus was reduced to quivering silence as Odysseus displayed by torchlight the first hand, the East–West cards curtained off, and told him to make four hearts on the ace of diamonds lead, adding that it was quite makeable, with trumps breaking normally, and any essential finesses working:

♠ A J 8 6 3
♡ Q J 10 3
◊ J 3
♣ Q J

♠ K Q 10
♡ A 8 6 5 2
◊ Q 5
♣ K 8 7

Rhesus was told that the ace of diamonds encouraged the 10 from East; and even though he played the queen himself the king of diamonds followed, East completing his echo with the 2. A third diamond now followed, and Rhesus thought about it a while. Knowing the heart finesse was working, he didn't want his ace forced by the 9; and with the unexpected ruff and sluff he might be able to discard a club from hand and two more on the long spades. If he could make five, Apollo must surely be impressed! Accordingly, he trumped with the queen, but to his annoyance East played a third diamond; and with the unnecessary promotion now had to make a trump trick with his 9 as well as the ace of clubs. The East–West hands were revealed:

♠ 7 2   ♠ 9 5 4
♡ 7   ♡ K 9 4
◊ A K 9 8 7 6   ◊ 10 4 2
♣ 6 4 3 2   ♣ A 10 9 5

"Alas," said Odysseus sadly. "Like Narcissus, thou hast been misled by the false Echo, for with a seven-card suit might not West have found a bid? Yet Apollo is just, and will not condemn his servant for one error. Perchance thou mayst regain all here." He turned the board over to reveal two more hands, the same conditions applying, and the contract again four hearts:

[48]

♠ J 10 3
♡ Q 5 2
◇ K 10 9 8
♣ A 5 4

♠ Q 9 2
♡ A K J 9 6 3
◇ J
♣ K J 3

This time the lead was the ace of spades, followed by the king. Then came the 4 of diamonds. Rhesus played low from dummy, and East won with the ace. Back came a small diamond, and Rhesus, like Oedipus, was at the cross-roads. He thought fleetingly of the possibility of a ruff, but with a seven-card suit East might have found a bid, and in any case West was surely marked with the queen of diamonds. The greater danger, bearing in mind the previous hand, was a trump promotion for the defenders, and thus he decided to throw his apparently losing club. When West ruffed, the contract was again one down, the defenders' hands being:

♠ A K 8 6	♠ 7 5 4
♡ 10 8 7	♡ 4
◇ 4	◇ A Q 7 6 5 3 2
♣ 10 9 7 6 2	♣ Q 8

"Alas," said Odysseus sadly. "Again thou hast fallen for the oldest palimpsest in the parchment. Did we not say that *trumps* were breaking quite normally? Do not the odds therefore favour ruffing high? Thy fears of promotion must surely indicate an unreadiness for responsibility at the top. Much as it grieves the god, Apollo must look upon his servant's offer to serve with anathema, and forbid him the role. Thou shalt live, yet shalt thou be punished for thy presumption."

So saying, we extinguished the torches and flitted from the tent. And there, quietly grazing, were the two mares of Rhesus, Trixi and Peggy. As quickly as we could we untied them, and flew back (figuratively speaking) to the Greek camp, not even pausing at the Scamander River to let them drink. The rosy dawn was already fingering the sky as we returned in triumph, to waken Agamemnon from his top-like torpor, and tell our tale. Our great commander, naturally, was at first annoyed that we had disobeyed his curfew, but on hearing our full report appreciated the importance of what we had done, and finally gave us his mixed blessing.

"Well done," he said. "There may even be promotion for you in this. At the very least, as the Titans would say, it's been a night to remember. Paris and Hector will be furious when the offer of sponsorship is withdrawn, so we'll still have a battle on our hands, especially," he added, suddenly seeing the problem, "when they see those animals here and work out what really happened – a flying mare will be the least of their threats. And one more thing: it's all very well punishing Rhesus by nicking his neddies and riding off into the sunrise, but this is supposed to be a bridge tournament, not a bloody war. What in the name of Chronos are we going to do with two horses?"

XI

The Wrath of Achilles

Note: Achilles, mightiest of the Greeks, was still offended with Agamemnon and refused to fight, but finally agreed that his friend Patroclus might wear his armour, provided that he did not pursue the Trojans to their walls. In the heat of battle Patroclus disregarded these instructions, and was killed by Hector. Achilles, grieving for the death of his friend, and further incensed by the appearance of Hector in that sumptuous armour, had new armour made for himself by the smith Hephaestus (Homer describes it at considerable length), and stormed into battle. In bitter conflict he slew Hector, tied the corpse to his chariot, and dragged the body thrice about the walls of Troy. Such rage might seem to us excessive, but the wrath of Achilles had been greatly aroused by the unmentionable indignities which Hector in his triumph had inflicted upon his foes. . .

Achilles, still unwilling to turn out against the Trojans, had nevertheless requested a rubber or two with Briseis, but Agamemnon, offended by his refusal to play, had crudely sent back the message that a man with no lead in his pencil didn't need a rubber. His pride injured, Achilles retired further into his tent, and the impasse continued. In desperation we consulted the Oracle, only to receive the enigmatic response, TIME WOUNDS ALL HEELS.

The big match was almost upon us, and we were short of heroes. The Ajax-Aias combination had temporarily cracked up, and Patroclus had been entirely unsuccessful in his attempts to entice Achilles into play ("With a hand like this, who needs a partner?" had been his only response). The best he could get was the promise that should he, Patroclus, be selected, then he, Achilles, would lend him his precious good-luck tortoise (on condition it didn't get away – it would be impossible to catch). Agamemnon finally made his selection for the first half: Odysseus and I would do battle in the open field, while Patroclus and Aias, keen but untried, would enter into closed combat. It was, we agreed, the only possible compromise, and Patroclus and Aias, the former carefully clutching Zeno, went off to do battle with Paris and Hector.

A few hours later they emerged, shaken, ashen-faced, and empty-handed. Odysseus and I had had a reasonable set, we thought, and were certainly not prepared to find ourselves down 72 IMPs at the half. Hector, it seemed, had been in devastating form, and had simply slaughtered Patroclus. He and Aias had begun tolerably well, but had then got a bit too confident, and on Board 13 Patroclus had rashly disputed Hector's claim, wagering Zeno against the Trojan blue bunny, and from that moment on, without their lucky mascot, they had done nothing right at all.

Board 13 was not without interest. Odysseus and I had cheerfully bid the obvious six hearts, but unable to cope with the 4–0 trump split had gone one down. Hector, however, was playing in six no trumps, and had not only made the contract but had also added insult to injury by spreading his hand after the spade lead hit the table:

Board 13
All Vulnerable

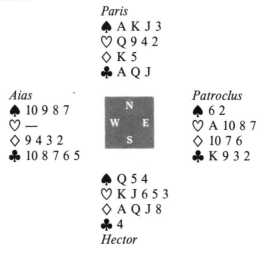

Paris
♠ A K J 3
♡ Q 9 4 2
◇ K 5
♣ A Q J

Aias
♠ 10 9 8 7
♡ —
◇ 9 4 3 2
♣ 10 8 7 6 5

Patroclus
♠ 6 2
♡ A 10 8 7
◇ 10 7 6
♣ K 9 3 2

♠ Q 5 4
♡ K J 6 5 3
◇ A Q J 8
♣ 4
Hector

Patroclus, sitting with the heart stack and the king of clubs, disputed the claim. The side-bet was agreed, and Hector proceeded to cash out. "Obviously," he began, "you must have all four hearts and the king of clubs to even contemplate an objection, but. . ." – Patroclus broke in, a little too eagerly, to point out that even if this were so Hector could not assume it, and must state a line of play that would succeed regardless of distribution.

"As I was about to say," Hector continued, picking up the tortoise and placing it in an unspeakable position beneath his blue bunny, "my claim does not depend on that. If hearts break, there are always twelve tricks, and if there are four in West's hand I can safety-play the suit. I hope," he added with heavy sarcasm, "I don't have to explain that?" Patroclus nodded, not quite so confident now.

Hector went on. "If, however, East has the hearts, twelve tricks are there on either the club finesse, or a squeeze and end-play. . ." – "But," Aias interrupted, "you can't choose which. . ."

"Nonsense," retorted Hector. "As Plato would say, it's completely immaterial. I win the ace of spades, and lead a heart to the king. I assume," he added ironically, "you won't make it easy for me by flying with the ace at once? And when I get the bad news I simply cash out four rounds of spades, then three rounds of diamonds, ending in hand. There are minor variations should anyone show out too soon, but basically I reduce East's hand and dummy to the same shape, thus." He pulled out a few cards from each hand:

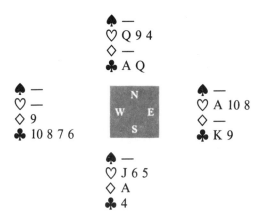

```
                    ♠ —
                    ♡ Q 9 4
                    ◇ —
                    ♣ A Q

    ♠ —                              ♠ —
    ♡ —            N                 ♡ A 10 8
    ◇ 9        W       E             ◇ —
    ♣ 10 8 7 6        S              ♣ K 9

                    ♠ —
                    ♡ J 6 5
                    ◇ A
                    ♣ 4
```

"And when I lead the ace of diamonds," he concluded, "East has had it completely. I throw the queen of clubs and watch you wriggle. If you throw a heart, I make two hearts and the ace of clubs; while if you throw a club, I cash the ace, then exit with the queen of hearts. If you take it, you're end-played; if you don't, I lead up to the jack. As you can see, it doesn't matter in the least whether you've got the king of clubs or not."

After their dismal exhibition Patroclus and Aias scarcely felt like watching the second half, let alone playing. And as Agamemnon sat slowly contemplating his options, wondering whether he should play himself and Menelaus, there came a sudden roar from Achilles's tent. Patroclus had just broken the news about the loss of 72 IMPs, and, more significantly, Zeno. The final bellow, we subsequently learnt, was in response to the ultimate indignity which Hector had imposed upon it. In fury, Achilles burst from his tent, and demanded the right to play. The second half would thus find Odysseus and me in closed combat, and Achilles with Menelaus (the latter under strict instructions not to bid no trumps) in the open field.

Achilles prepared himself carefully for the coming encounter. He filled out his convention card with great ceremony, and borrowed from Hephaestus a sharp pencil (with lead in it), and a cunningly-wrought scoring tablet with the records of past tournaments graven upon it. Odysseus and I had long disappeared into the enclosed arena, but when the call to open conflict came Achilles pronounced himself ready.

The Trojans, having heard the news, elected to set Paris and Hector against Achilles, leaving us to deal with Aeneas and Antenor. We acquitted ourselves with valour, as did they, and there was little in it either way. Yet as we returned to the open arena, to look upon the hands we had already played, we found that not all was lost. Achilles had been in amazing form! With only six hands to go, the difference was down to 24 IMPs, and as we entered the amphitheatre a burst of cheering signalled yet another unlikely three no trumps. But the real news, we were told, concerned the side-bet. Achilles had publicly demanded the return of his pet, but Hector had informed him, mockingly, that it was destined for soup, and the two had almost come to blows. Achilles had expressed his total contempt for Hector and Paris, had thrust his pencil up the blue bunny, and vowed that he would defeat the Trojans or forsake the game forever. In reply, Hector had stated that if he lost a 72 IMP lead to a lout like Achilles he would do likewise, and the end result was a guarantee that one or the other would take no further part in the conflict. And Achilles, over the first twenty boards, had made the impossible seem merely improbable.

But when the last board hit the screen Odysseus and I felt less jubilant. We were still (though unbeknown to Achilles) five IMPs behind, and on that board Aeneas and Antenor had bid the cold four hearts and made their ten tricks. We might pick up an IMP or two, but with three top losers no contract looked any better. We had reckoned without the might of Achilles:

[54]

Board 26
All Vulnerable

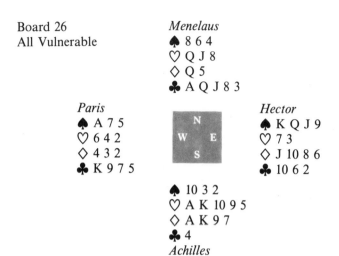

Menelaus
♠ 8 6 4
♡ Q J 8
♢ Q 5
♣ A Q J 8 3

Paris
♠ A 7 5
♡ 6 4 2
♢ 4 3 2
♣ K 9 7 5

Hector
♠ K Q J 9
♡ 7 3
♢ J 10 8 6
♣ 10 6 2

♠ 10 3 2
♡ A K 10 9 5
♢ A K 9 7
♣ 4
Achilles

The bidding, like Menelaus, was short and simple:

1♡	...	4♡
4♠	...	5♣
6♡		

Paris, on lead, toyed with the ace of spades, but uncertain of the apparent cue bid finally led a more neutral trump. It still looked like only ten tricks, but Achilles without hesitation won the king of hearts; took the club finesse; cashed the ace of clubs, tossing the 3 of spades; ruffed a club; returned to dummy with a trump; ruffed another club to set up the jack; and drew the last trump, to leave this position:

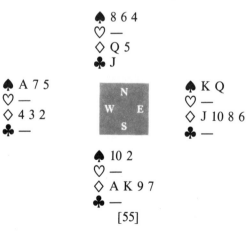

♠ 8 6 4
♡ —
♢ Q 5
♣ J

♠ A 7 5
♡ —
♢ 4 3 2
♣ —

♠ K Q
♡ —
♢ J 10 8 6
♣ —

♠ 10 2
♡ —
♢ A K 9 7
♣ —

[55]

The queen of diamonds was now cashed; and the jack of clubs followed. Hector was forced to toss the queen of spades, Achilles the 10, and Paris a small diamond. When the last diamond was played from the table, Hector had to cover, and Achilles won the king, to leave these cards:

♠ 8 6 4
♡ —
◇ —
♣ —

♠ A 7 5   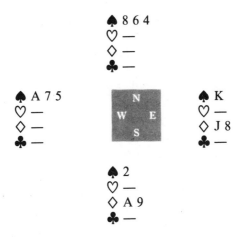   ♠ K
♡ —   ♡ —
◇ —   ◇ J 8
♣ —   ♣ —

♠ 2
♡ —
◇ A 9
♣ —

The coup-de-grace was the 2 of spades: Paris could take it, and be end-played in spades; or he could let it run to Hector, who would be end-played in diamonds. Being the man he was he ducked, and left to Hector the ignominy of conceding the last two tricks.

The Greek contingent roared in disbelief! We had come from nowhere to win the premier event on the final board, and, an extra bonus, Hector, mightiest of our foes, would play no more. Paris took it badly, stomping out and promising the lion-hearted Achilles a short if glorious life, but Hector was gallant in defeat, not even criticising his partner's last lead, graciously returning Zeno from the kitchens, conceding the match without bitterness, and making a short funeral oration in which he declared that the game was becoming rather a drag anyway.

"That's as may be," said Odysseus sagely, as we watched Achilles being lionised, "but the boot may soon be on the other foot, so to speak. Remember what the Oracle said: Paris is no pussy-foot, and I for one wouldn't like to be in Achilles's shoes the next time they meet."

XII

The Olympiad

Note: After the deaths of Patroclus and Hector, the Greeks made ready the funeral preparations (Achilles sacrificing a dozen of the youth of Troy to the memory of his friend). These were followed by the Games, a precursor of the later Olympics. The events included boxing, a foot race, a spear fight, the discus, the javelin, archery, and a wrestling match (in which Ajax and Achilles fought to a draw – though who took first prize of a Tripod and who the second prize of a woman valued at four oxen is a matter for some conjecture). The premier event was the chariot race, the winner of which was to receive a fine prize (but even the last placed a two-handled pan). The team urged on by Diomedes won this event, but the manner of their "victory" forms a unique chapter in the history of the Games. . .

Apollo's golden rays had kindled the sacred flame on Mount Olympus, and the mighty torch, relayed by glowing youths, was now on its way to the stadium. All hostilities were to cease for the duration of the games, and, celebrating Hector's departure from the competition, we relaxed around our campfires till the flame should come; drinking by night till we were tight as Andronicus, unwinding by day in the Pierian Springs. It was not, we decided bemusedly, the best of all possible preparation, and with the Opening Ceremony drawing nigh a little panic set in. We made sacrifices to the gods (Achilles, perhaps, rather too zealously), but the words of the Oracle were not altogether reassuring:

> *Defeat and triumph, two impostors:*
> *Treat them just the same.*
> *Not one victory shall be yours,*
> *Yet yours the greater gain.*

Even Odysseus was puzzled at this, and we concluded gloomily that it must be along the lines of the Delphic know-thyself nonsense, that more-important-to-take-part-than-to-win sort of thing. We weren't enthused.

When the order of events was proclaimed, a slight buzz of

[57]

anticipation could be heard. As usual, Phlogiston Chariots were sponsoring the Teams, and their prize list included a glorious Golden Bowl as well as the usual motley collection of tripods, mares and female slaves; but they had also offered a brass pan and wooden spoon for the team finishing last – the ignominy would be considerable. Even more controversial were the prizes for the Individual: Delphic Oracles, Ltd., had offered their usual Tripod for First, but had not forseen that Cumae Prophecies, Inc., would steal their fire by offering for Second one Golden Bough, complete with Vestal Virgin. Competition for second would thus be intense (as it were), and many were the jokes of the first-prize-one-week-at-Philippi-second-prize-two variety.

When the entries were called for the Teams, six doughty champions stepped forth. Eight had originally entered, but the withdrawal of the Slavs and Ostrogoths had weakened the field considerably. There had been a late entry from some wandering Jews, but Agamemnon, always suspicious of possible female participation ("A name like 'Hur'," he was heard to mutter) had ruled against them, somewhat ambiguously, for having the wrong kinds of helmets and being too much withdrawn ("What you might call a circumscribed existence," Odysseus explained). Lots were drawn, and the teams arranged themselves in order:

A. The Trojans, led by Paris; seasoned war-horses all, and odds-on favourites for the event.

B. Representing the Far East, a team from distant Cathay; well-disciplined, identically matched, and likely (it was whispered) to cause some confucian.

Γ. From far-off Albion, beyond the rolling Roman woad, the unknown Blue Team; wryly disparaged as 'The Cold Bottoms', yet pict by the pundits to scotch a few hopes.

Δ. And from the Near East, Caliph Omar and his sponsored team of all-star Arabians; determined to be on Vu-Graph as much as possible.

E. From beyond the Pillars of Hercules, the Atlantis Aces; destined to cause a few upsets.

Ω. And neither last nor least, we hoped, the fighting Greeks; myself and Menelaus, teamed up with Palamedes and young Aias.

The first rounds began, disastrously for us. Unable to hold back the Atlantides or unscrew the Inscrutables, we went down to both by a score of 16 to 14. The Trojans meanwhile were in devastating form, first smashing China 25 to 0, and then sweeping aside the Near

[58]

Easterners in the same manner. In the other matches, the Near East had proved too hot for the Blues, who were scorched 25 to 1; but the Blues in turn salvaged both points and respectability in reducing the Aces to rubble, 25 to 1. The day thus ended with the Trojans triumphant, and the rest of us licking our various wounds.

Meanwhile, the Individual was reaching its climax. It was being played on a board-a-match basis, with a predetermined par: one point for winning the board, and half for a tie. As the day drew to its weary close, Ajax and Odysseus found themselves to the fore on equal points, and, as Fate would have it, pitted against each other in the final round – Ajax paired with a competent Visigoth, and Odysseus with an able but nervous Armenian. The outcome would thus depend on the last bout of all, and it was with some trepidation that the four contestants slowly raised their hands. The preliminaries were brief: Ajax opened one club (basic Gordian), which Odysseus doubled (intending to raise his partner's suit too high, and thus avoid the blame for actually going down), after which everybody passed. The contract was thus to be one club, doubled, and played by Ajax:

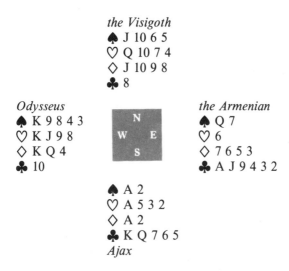

the Visigoth
♠ J 10 6 5
♡ Q 10 7 4
◇ J 10 9 8
♣ 8

Odysseus
♠ K 9 8 4 3
♡ K J 9 8
◇ K Q 4
♣ 10

the Armenian
♠ Q 7
♡ 6
◇ 7 6 5 3
♣ A J 9 4 3 2

♠ A 2
♡ A 5 3 2
◇ A 2
♣ K Q 7 6 5
Ajax

Odysseus led the king of hearts, which Ajax, unsuspecting, won with the ace. But as he pondered the lead, the drachma dropped – Odysseus, first of heroes, this time wanted to be second. Well, two could play at that game! He therefore returned the king of clubs, which the Armenian, impervious to Odysseus's glare, won with the ace. A diamond was returned, and ducked all round to dummy's 8. Ajax now came off the table with the jack of spades, covered by the queen, ducked by declarer, and won by the king. Two tricks all. Back came the 9 of spades, won perforce by Ajax's ace; and on his return of the club 7 Odysseus dumped the king of diamonds, while the Armenian, confused and not yet comprehending, won with the 9. Three all. The diamond return was won by Ajax with the ace, Odysseus dropped the queen; and a small heart led, Odysseus's 8 holding the trick until his partner, presuming he should be on lead, trumped small (noting the smile of approval from West). Four all. Back came another diamond, Ajax trumping dummy's winner with the queen of clubs, Odysseus tossing his highest heart. Back came another small heart, and the Armenian, more confused than ever, again ruffed his partner's trick. Five all. Back came the last diamond, and again Ajax ruffed his winner high; and exited at trick 12 with his last heart. The Armenian, about to trump with Pluto's bedposts and cash the jack for the setting trick, suddenly became aware of Odysseus's dark brow and face of thunder. In a flash he saw all, and, faced with the choice of being crushed by Ajax or exterminated by Odysseus, wisely chose the former as the lesser evil. He threw down the jack of clubs, and exited like forked lightning: the 4 of clubs to Ajax's 5; and himself to Mount Ararat and the safety of whatever Ark he could find. One club, doubled, making, for plus 140; the result a stand-off, as the designated outcome was two hearts making three. There was much discussion of the hand about the campfires that night, and many a wager laid as to how the prize would be.

The next day dawned clear, and the next rounds began. Again we battled valiantly, but to no avail: Omar's Circus played to the crowd, riding roughshod over us 17–13; and, battered and bruised, we could not cope with the Blues and their bewildering array of Tartan and Multicoloured bids, again losing 17–13. Four matches now, without a single victory, and the results getting worse. Our only consolation was that the Trojans, whom we had yet to meet, had celebrated too late and too soon the night before, and had been trounced 25–0, first by the Blues and then by the Aces. And in the other matches the carnage continued: first, the Gang of Four purged the Aces, 25–0; then, inexplicably changing their system, went down 25–2 to Omar's All-Stars. Again, it was a weary and battered contingent that crawled home to recover for the final round in the morning.

Other results kept coming in. As expected, Pheidippides came through the Marathon in fine fettle; Leander was first across the

[60]

Hellespont, to a hero's welcome; and Hyacinth's special training struck gold in the Discus. But there were surprises as well: the hammer throw was won by an unknown giant from the frozen North ("I was loki," he said in his strange accent); Cassius eliminated all rivals in the Boxing at the Capitol ("Imperious Caesar dead and turned to Clay," he chortled); while the Decapathon, unexpectedly, went to a couple of blockheads from Gaul ("Hellas est omnis divisa in partes duo," quipped one as he received his myrtle wreath). And the curtains of day were duly drawn.

The next day found us in resolute mood. We might not gain the garland, but our names were not to be carved in the wooden spoon! And now we faced the Trojans, who, smarting from their defeats of yesterday, would be giving no quarter. We took our places, Menelaus and I set against Aeneas and Antenor, leaving Palamedes and Aias to hold off Paris and Troilus. Menelaus and I did well, and but for a wheel coming off early in the round (Menelaus bidding the no trumps first, and therefore having to play the hand) would have been comfortably in the lead; for we had finished well, ripping off a vulnerable three no trumps on 20 points in the final straight:

Board 13
All Vulnerable

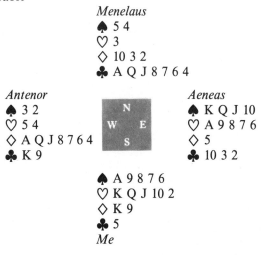

Menelaus
♠ 5 4
♡ 3
♢ 10 3 2
♣ A Q J 8 7 6 4

Antenor
♠ 3 2
♡ 5 4
♢ A Q J 8 7 6 4
♣ K 9

Aeneas
♠ K Q J 10
♡ A 9 8 7 6
♢ 5
♣ 10 3 2

♠ A 9 8 7 6
♡ K Q J 10 2
♢ K 9
♣ 5
Me

Menelaus opened three clubs, and I had a fling at three no trumps. When the queen of diamonds was led to my King, I had little option

[61]

but to try for the doubleton king of clubs onside, scurrying home with nine tricks when it was (yes, I could have made more, but nine looked good enough for me). I was hence rather dismayed when the scores were called out to find our +600 matched by 600 at the other table; we were desperately disappointed to find that we had lost the match 20–10; and we were even more disgusted to find that this was enough to put the Trojans in first place overall, leaving us at the very bottom (the Paper Tigers having shredded the Celts 25–0, and the swells from Atlantis swamping the Nile Deltas the same way). We had not managed a single victory (as the Oracle had predicted), and the final tabulation read:

		A	B	Γ	Δ	E	Ω	Total	Placing
Trojans	A	X	25	0	25	0	20	70	1st
Cathay	B	0	X	25	2	25	16	68	2nd=
Blues	Γ	25	0	X	1	25	17	68	2nd=
Near East	Δ	0	25	25	X	0	17	67	4th=
Aces	E	25	0	1	25	X	16	67	4th=
Greeks	Ω	10	14	13	13	14	X	64	Last

Disconsolately we waited to hear the wooden spoon rattling in the brass pan, ringing out to all the news of our discomfiture, when who should come by but smug Odysseus (having, it later transpired, persuaded the judges to disqualify him in the final round). He had no need to ask how we had done, for every barbarian was jeering at our expense. Instead, he looked over the results sheets, and then, more closely, at Board 13. "Curious hand," he observed. "As Athena's Owl might say, both sides can make three no trumps on the lead of a minor queen. But if you lead anything else you get nine tricks in defence before they ever get in. Tragic. Who was the goat?"

Palamedes and I replied simultaneously: "Not me. I was playing the hand." We stopped, looked at one another in disbelief as the clouds unfolded, then grabbed at the sheets again. Sure enough, three no trumps was making for us both East–West and North–South, and instead of an even board we had a plus of 1200, or a gain of 15 IMPs.

Anxiously we recalculated the results, our initial disappointment in finding that our 20–10 loss became merely a 15–15 tie swiftly changing to jubilation as we realised that the five Victory Points thus gained would move us into First place overall (69), and knock the Trojans back to Last (65).

Predictably, the Trojans refused to accept the result on the grounds that the scores had been officially decreed and were hence final. But the Pantheon ruled otherwise, and the Golden Bowl was ours. There were fireworks at the end, of course, with the Trojans boycotting the Closing Ceremony, and Paris, brandishing his bow of burning gold, declaring that we were cads and bounders riding for a fall.

"Talk about Chariots of Fire," declared Odysseus, as the Trojans stormed from the stadium. "And so much for 'See you in Salonika'. There's going to be Charon to pay over the way things have panned out here – as the Bard says, eats is eats and stew is stew, and ne'er the twain should meat – but Paris isn't going to like a taste of the wooden spoon when he could have been drinking out of the Golden Bowl. This isn't going to be a green and pleasant land for long."

XIII

Ruin-Maker

Note: There was in Troy a celebrated statue of Athena, a gift from the goddess herself, and it was believed that the city would not be taken as long as the Palladium, as it was called, remained within the walls. Odysseus and Diomedes therefore secretly entered the city, disguised as beggars, and though they were recognised by Helen (who for some reason chose not to betray them), they succeeded in obtaining the statue and carrying it back to the Grecian camp. Later traditions also suggest that on the way back Odysseus tried to murder Diomedes, so as to gain all the credit for the exploit for himself; but that is somewhat of a misrepresentation, as is revealed by the inside story of this majestic secret service, the full details of which have up to now remained classified information. . .

Odysseus had called for a special meeting of the Council, and everyone except Achilles turned up. Something had to be done, as the Trojans were still holding out strongly, and he had, the wily one modestly declaimed, thought of a special plan that would ensure the triumph of our forces in the coming sessions.

"Not that crazy wooden horse idea again," Agamemnon broke in roughly. "You know that would never work." But Odysseus assured him, no, nothing like that at all. It was well known, he explained, that the superstitious Trojans believed that all their luck came from a trophy called the Palladium, given to them (in pre-Judgement days) by Athena. If we could, he went on, sneak into their club-rooms and make off with it, they'd be completely demoralised and there'd be no stopping us. "And what better time," he continued, "than their club night tomorrow? We'll send over a pair, ostensibly to settle the conditions for the coming encounter, and make sure that we get invited to play."

"But how will that help?" asked Menelaus (M). "It's all very well getting into their club-rooms, but there's bond, I mean, bound to be a guard over the trophy itself."

"Aha!" Odysseus smiled triumphantly. "We'll need a diversion, and that's where you come in, as my partner." I suddenly realised that he was looking at me, but before the buckles on my breast could burst with pride he added something completely unnecessary about being

[64]

the most dispensable should anything go wrong. Still, I had to admit the plan had chances.

"What is needed," Odysseus went on, "is for you to play a hand which is so spectacular that even the guards and directors will be distracted while I as dummy sneak off, responding to the call of the wild or whatever, grab the trophy, and head for the ships. And I have just the hand for it – one of them will have 31 points, but there'll be seven clubs on our way, and if I get smart, as they say, or you act quite normally, we can probably get doubled and REDOUBLED." He spread out the following hands:

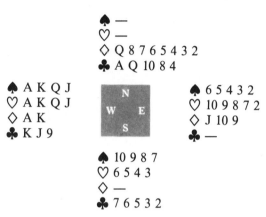

♠ —
♡ —
◇ Q 8 7 6 5 4 3 2
♣ A Q 10 8 4

♠ A K Q J
♡ A K Q J
◇ A K
♣ K J 9

♠ 6 5 4 3 2
♡ 10 9 8 7 2
◇ J 10 9
♣ —

♠ 10 9 8 7
♡ 6 5 4 3
◇ —
♣ 7 6 5 3 2

"Wait a moment," said Tiresias slowly. "I've seen a hand like that somewhere before. Or is it in the future? I get awfully muddled these days. That Flemish fellow isn't it? Royal Cansino, you know – clubs and another suit; or From Colchis with Love – Goldfleecer. . . Oh, thunderballs, I just can't remember. But what if they've read it too?"

"Trojans don't read," said Odysseus confidently. "That's why they're Trojans. Word deriving from 'Trogs'. Besides, even if they do recognise the hand the diversion will be that much greater, and ditto my chances. Though not yours," he added to me, reassuringly.

Well, all went according to plan at first. We made our way into broad-streeted Troy, were invited to play at the Palladium, and, sure enough, just after supper I saw wily Odysseus swap the board (all vulnerable) for the prepared one he was carrying beneath his tunic. But when I picked up the hand, a sinking feeling rose (pardon the expression) as I saw: 6 5 4 3 2, 10 9 8 7 2, J 10 9, —. The cards had been put into the wrong pockets! Odysseus looked at his 31 points, turned faintly white, and excused himself from the table before the bidding had even started (feeling, I hoped, genuinely ill). Topless Helen was called in to take his place, and her eyes went wider than her cleavage as she tried to count her points. The bidding began: two clubs from Helen; two no trumps from Troilus, North (highly unusual); three desperate spades from me; four clubs from Cresseid (hoping to get doubled); six spades from Helen (silly woman, doesn't she know whose side she's on?); seven clubs from Troilus; a mesmerised seven spades from me, thinking of the oil Agamemnon would boil us in; double from Cresseid; REDOUBLE from Helen. End of the affair.

Well, as you can see, it comes in from the cold on any lead, provided that East plays the hand (I was only obeying orders), and as long as diamonds are forever untouched (I knew better). And with seven clubs REDOUBLED making North–South, the potential swing on the board was 4,500. I shall not enter into the gory and inglorious details of how I managed to crawl home, where I found Odysseus and the others exulting over the capture of the Palladium (its loss hadn't been discovered when they threw me, like Andromache's bouncing baby boy, from the walls of Troy, or I wouldn't have made it at all). They've let Homer come and visit me on my sick-bed, and he says he'll do what he can to immortalise me for my bit in the affair – honour galore, and all that – but (this is for your eyes only) I've quite frankly had enough of heroism for a while. Live and let die is all very well for the Big Boys, but give me a warm bed and a good thriller any day.

XIV

Odysseus Faces a Restricted Choice

Note: When Menelaus called upon the chieftains of Greece to honour their pledge and help him win back Helen, they all came forward without reluctance, except for Odysseus, who, married to Penelope and happy in his wife and child, had no great desire for the troublesome affair. A messenger was therefore sent to urge him forth, but when Palamedes arrived in Ithaca Odysseus pretended to be mad, yoking together an ox and an ass to his plough, and sowing salt into the sands. To test him, Palamedes placed the infant Telemachus before the plough, whereupon Odysseus turned aside, showing thereby that he was no madman, and therefore bound to keep his pledge. Years later, to avenge himself, Odysseus concealed gold in Palamedes's tent, and, forging a letter from Priam, had Palamedes accused of treachery and condemned to be stoned to death. Odysseus does not emerge well out of this miserable affair, yet, when all the circumstances are taken into consideration, Palamedes too must take some of the blame. . .

The sun did not shine, it was too wet to play, so we sat in our tents all that cold cold wet day. I sat there with Aias, we sat there we two, and said how we wished we had something to do. Too wet to go out, and too cold to play whist, so we sat round the fire and slowly got – sorry, looked out at the mist. Then something went BUMP! – by Zeuss, did we jump. We looked and saw Menelaus flat on the mat – one man down and another guy gone. But he picked himself up and came in with fat cat Palamedes, the two of them taking off their helmets and noisily blowing the raindrops from their noses. "Shhh," warned Aias, and pointed to the back of the tent where Odysseus lay curled up in some skins, getting in some sleep before going out to direct. And a miserable time he'd be having of it – lice in the tunic and a cold in his nose. Talk about Trojan wall blues!

Palamedes drew up a stool, and helped himself generously from our amphora. Typical that, not even asking . . . not that we minded, mind, but . . . He smacked his lips, happily, poured himself another, and looked out through the flap where the rain was still coming down faster than Helen's drawers – sorry, must watch these military metaphors. For a while we sat in silence, then Palamedes remarked drily that it was one of those days that made you wish you were at home, wishing you were here. There passed through my mind a fleeting vision of Argos, my little white home in the west with its Persian carpets and Phoenician blinds, and my faithful wife Aegialeia, anxiously awaiting my return – but I resolutely set it aside: we were men with a mission, we had no choice.

Noting our despondency, Palamedes tried to cheer us up with the latest Cretan jokes: what do you call a dog with no legs? Doesn't matter, it won't come anyway. Or, what do you call five Cretans standing together? A thicket. Then, what was the Cretan philosopher doing in the middle of his meadow? Someone had told him that if he wanted to be a genius, he had to be out-standing in his field. And, how do you titillate an ocelot. You oscillate his ti – "That reminds me," young Aias suddenly broke in. "Standing in his field, I mean. How *did* you get Odysseus to come? The way he was going on earlier, with his turn of duty coming up and the rain down, wishing you steeped in the deepest shade of Hades. How did you do it?"

Palamedes looked round cautiously at the sleeping figure of Odysseus before lowering his voice in reply. "It wasn't easy," he chuckled. "But it had to be done, or my name was middle up down. You know how depressed he gets at times – says every time he sees a cemetery full of grave-stones that it reminds him of the Cadmus story, only backwards – living men sown, dragon's teeth coming up. Anyway, he'd originally said he was unavailable because of the farm, and because young Telemachus was teething – *aro, non armo*, as Cadmus might say – but to tell the truth (*in viro veritas*, as it were), I think he was a bit concerned about snaky Antinous hanging around Penelope – 'he don't like his manners, he don't like his face'. He wasn't going, and that was that. And nothing I could say would make him change his mind. Then *fiat lux*, as they say at the chariot wash – I had the bright idea of an offer he couldn't refuse: Antinous and I against him and Penelope, the best of five rubbers, thirteen months in the fields against a short stint at Troy.

"Antinous was on – with the cat away, the rat could play; Penelope was only too keen to get rid of him – Antinous, that is; and the thought of yoking the pair of us to the plough for a year or so was too much for Odysseus to resist – so before you could say *annos ludendo hausi*, years of ludo and housie, the game was up. Odysseus wasn't too worried, and the way Antinous played the first hand I could see why – so I had to insist on certain basics: follow suit, no playing for

[68]

overtricks, always show the count. And it seemed to work reasonably well, until at two rubbers each, everyone vulnerable, and the points above the line about equal, the crunch came – the neatest example of restricted choice that I've seen in a good long while."

"Restricted choice?" asked Menelaus, puzzled. "What's that? You mean, like when I'm playing with Achilles not being allowed to bid no trumps?"

Palamedes tried to explain, but words like 'entelechy', 'pre-established harmony', 'ghostly paradigm of things', and 'actuality of the potential-as-possible contingent on a-priori necessity rather than Democritan atomism and a-posteriori factuality' were a bit too much for any of us, let alone Menelaus, so I broke in to explain. "In words of one syllable," I said, "it means that the odds most of the time with a choice of plays stay what they were at the start of the hand, and do not change with the play of the cards." Menelaus looked as if he wanted to argue, but Palamedes quickly scribbled down a hand, and took up the tale again:

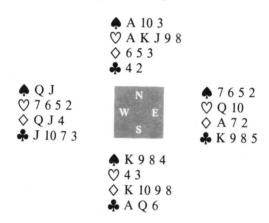

```
              ♠ A 10 3
              ♡ A K J 9 8
              ◇ 6 5 3
              ♣ 4 2

♠ Q J                        ♠ 7 6 5 2
♡ 7 6 5 2        N           ♡ Q 10
◇ Q J 4      W       E       ◇ A 7 2
♣ J 10 7 3       S           ♣ K 9 8 5

              ♠ K 9 8 4
              ♡ 4 3
              ◇ K 10 9 8
              ♣ A Q 6
```

"Odysseus was playing the hand in three no trumps, which, with nothing left to lose, and hoping to sow confusion, I doubled – maybe Penelope would take out into something, anything; but no, with a touching faith in her lord and master she REDOUBLED, and there we weren't (as they say in Utopia). So I prayed and played for a miracle, and led the 5 of hearts. Odysseus tried the 8, and lost to the Queen (Antinous, as ordered, showing the count). Back came a small spade, Odysseus played low, and I put in the queen. Odysseus looked at it suspiciously, but won the ace and ran the 10, losing to my jack. With nothing better to do, I carried on with the 2 of hearts, and Odysseus must have taken about ten years before he put in the 9 and lost to the 10."

"But why on earth—" began Menelaus, only to be brushed aside by Palamedes.

"You can see his problem, can't you? The original heart lead now looks like something rather than nothing, fourth best from a five card suit, since nobody in his right mind would have played the queen from the Q–10 on the first trick. So if he plays off the top hearts, he sets up a trick for me; but by taking the finesse, running the hearts, and exiting with a diamond he's almost certainly got nine tricks. No, the odds must favour the finesse, so you can imagine his fury at finding himself three light, vulnerable and REDOUBLED, 1600 down on a hand that was cold for game."

"For slam, you mean," Menelaus broke in. "I'd have made twelve tricks."

In vain did Palamedes try to convince Menelaus that Odysseus had played the hand, if not correctly, at least with the odds; his chances being at worse 87½%, with restricted choice operative in spades and hearts, and perhaps even in diamonds. As Aias quietly observed, it was an interesting hand on the given defence, for the better the player the worse his probable result. And that hand had sewn it all up, for no matter what followed something like that could not be set aside. Even so, Menelaus remained unconvinced, and went on muttering about what a queer world it would be if the right way to play the hand meant making only six tricks while the wrong way made twelve.

"And you'd be right," broke in a voice from the corner. We looked around to find Odysseus nonchalantly shuffling both a pack of cards and to his feet. "There's too much of this theoretical nonsense around," he went on. "And as for this notion of a-priori expectation, of Platonic Forms and Ideals – as Aristophanes would say, they're for the birds. We live," he continued solemnly, "in the post-Heracleitan age, an age of uncertainty and changing probabilities – you never walk into the same hand twice." He casually dealt out the cards, and looked up at Palamedes. "My salt ration for a month against you doing my next turn of duty that Menelaus and I, playing basic Gordian with nothing knotty, can wrap up you and Aias, with all your fancy theories."

Palamedes hesitated, suspecting a trap; but one month's salary to one night's duty seemed more than reasonable odds, and he couldn't really justify a refusal after all that had been said. So the wine was

[70]

poured, and the cards were dealt. And, as if in defiance of Odyssean relativity, the same pattern seemed to be emerging (Palamedes at least thought so): two rubbers each, all vulnerable in the decider, and Odysseus to deal. For the last few hands he'd been complaining about the biting cold and ditto lice, so I was the only one to see his hand, holding the pack, dive into his tunic as if to scratch a particularly itchy spot. Once more the hands were dealt, and only when the jack of spades was led to his contract of three no trumps, doubled and REDOUBLED, did Palamedes have a sense of déjà-vu, as he observed his hand and that of dummy:

♠ A 10 3
♡ A K J 9 7
◇ 6 5 3
♣ 4 2

♠ K 9 8 4
♡ 4 3
◇ K 10 9 8
♣ A Q 6

Palamedes throught a while, and then with a cryptic "No option, hot critics decree!" went up with the ace, and ran the 10, losing to Odysseus's Queen. Predictably, back came the 5 of hearts, but Palamedes, not to be fooled twice, went up with the ace and smiled as Menelaus dropped the 10. He now cashed his spades, Odysseus throwing small cards; then confidently led his last heart to the king, expecting to drop the queen. But to his horror, Menelaus played small, and though Palamedes did his best to bring in the diamonds (small to the 8), constant club returns left him two tricks in arrears, with the rubber beyond redemption. The East–West hands were:

♠ Q J   ♠ 7 6 5 2
♡ Q 8 5 2   ♡ 10 6
◇ A Q 4   ◇ J 7 2
♣ J 10 7 3   ♣ K 9 8 5

Palamedes protested that he'd been framed; but when Menelaus (of all people) pointed out that the contract could have been made by dropping the spades and getting the hearts right ("My 10 looked suspicious," he added, without a conscious touch of irony),

[71]

Palamedes had to accept his fate. Odysseus gave him some final advice ("*Semper ubi sub ubi*, as they say across the cold Adriatic"), but Palamedes rightly gave him the cold shoulder, and with a martyred expression and one last brave farewell ("I may be some time"), disappeared into the frozen night. And when the others had gone I looked disapprovingly at Odysseus, already lying back luxuriously in his warm skins.

"That was a lousy trick," I began. "You stacked those cards to make Palamedes think he was playing the same hand again, you brought in that cold deck, and before that you attacked him quite unfairly on his principles of restricted choice. You know quite well that he's right. . ."

"Nonsense," retorted Odysseus, stretching himself comfortably. "Or, as your learned pal would say, *tauri excretio*. As for stacking the hand, let him who is without aim cast the first stone – we've all done that in our time. And you've got to admit, it's sometimes pleasant to stone a martyr. I simply gave him an option: he could have made the contract by playing like Menelaus and bashing out everything in sight; or by being fully consistent with his own principles, and ploughing straight ahead. *He* was the one who changed teams in mid-furrow, and he's probably cursing himself now for having done so." He paused, then went on. "I've been waiting for that opportunity for a long time, because he did for me in the first place, and I want him to live just long enough to regret it. *Illegitimis non carborundum*, as they say in the service – don't let the bastards grind you down. And as for his entelechies and probabilities – to be sure, there are theories at the bottom of his jargon, but you've got to take them *cum grano salis*, or you'll find yourself out of step with the way things really are. The real trouble with this world of ours," he concluded sententiously, "is not that it's entirely reasonable, nor that it's entirely unreasonable – the chief problem is that it's almost reasonable, but not quite. And the Menelauses of this world have enough problems simply following suit without confusing themselves further."

XV

Troilus is Discarded

Note: When Calchas, the Trojan priest, fled Troy and went over to the Greeks (knowing that Troy was doomed to fall), he left behind his daughter Cresseid. Troilus, one of the sons of Priam, fell in love with her, and with the help of her uncle Pandarus was able to win her favour. However, Calchas wanted his daughter with him, and Diomedes arranged an exchange for the captured Antenor. Though Cresseid had sworn eternal fidelity to Troilus she soon gave all her affections to Diomedes, and rejected her former lover. Another story tells how Cresseid, rejected by all, was later to die lingeringly of leprosy, but such tales are obviously fabrications, for not only are they mediaeval additions to the more ancient legends of Troy, but diligent research into their romantic origins has uncovered all. . .

CANTICLE THE FIRST

The moment she started to play at the Palladium, Troilus felt the dart of Eros prick his heart, and was determined to win her as his partner. He could remember her from their childhood days together at the Paideuma, and recalled with shame how he too had laughed at her straggly appearance and her schoolgirl howlers – the time, for instance, in Geometry, when she had defined a polygon as a dead parrot; and that other occasion, in Current Affairs, when she had denounced a certain Egyptian queen as "a scrumpet" (a comment worthy, said wise old Socrates with a rare flash of irony, to be included with a fanfare of strumpets and a jam of tarts in an anthology of prose). She had meant nothing to him then, and he had not thought of her for some years, but that evening, seeing her across a crowded room, he felt the first stirrings of a strange enchantment.

But how to make her his own? The Mixed Pairs were coming up, but lacking the courage to approach her directly he sought out Pandarus to ask his advice. Pandarus, in his usual garrulous way, urged caution. "I'd be careful," he began. "After all, you don't know who she's been playing with the last few years, and she's got a bit of a reputation as the good time that's been had by all, you know.

Briefless encounters, and all that. And the same with her bidding – opens light and goes light far too often." But seeing that Troilus was not in the least dissuaded, he went on. "Still, takes a wench to turn the head of a dolt, they say. If I were you I'd get her sympathy by appealing to her tender instincts. She's got a weakness for wounded heroes, you know, especially bold hairy ones. But you'd do. Not that she always gets it right," he digressed. "Her dad, Calchas, got her the job, you know, and one day he heard a scream outside his tent, and looked out to see a naked warrior disappearing into the distance, with Cresseid hot in pursuit swinging a steaming cauldron: 'No, no, Cressie,' he said wearily, 'I said, *prick his boil.*' She was a bit lucky to stay on after that, er, mess-up, especially when her old man started working for the Greeks. Anyway," he concluded, coming back to the point, "why don't you go out and get yourself wounded, not too badly, mind, but like the Fisher King, say, in the thigh or thereabouts, and I'm sure you'll find her only too willing to help. And after that it's entirely up to you."

Troilus went forth in happiness, and one sunny morning in the merry month of May did seek to encounter foe upon the field of Mars. Valiantly did he venture, but came a moment he was caught with trousers lowered, and wounded piteous sore. Rejoicing was he brought back to the citadel, forsooth, and there the fair Cresseid did tend his care, with questions many and oft concerning his sad sorrow.

"How did it happen?" she would ask, and he would tell her mighty deeds of arms and men, tales of wonder and of woe. "Is it sore?" she would inquire, laying her hand tenderly upon his wound, and leaving him at a loss for words. "Did it hurt when the dart went in?" she wanted to know, "did you feel a prick?" Troilus, embarrassed, admitted that he had certainly felt a bit foolish. "That is not what I meant at all," she replied, settling his pillow and showing him what she did. And the long and the short of it all was that she agreed to play with him in the Mixed Pairs, and left him bathed in gladness, crying, "What have I done to deserve this?"

*

CANTICLE THE SECOND

When the news reached our camp it was generally ignored, but Calchas of the calculating mind seemed strangely perturbed. It was not so much the fact of his daughter's new partnership that bothered him – he was used to that – but rather that something in the

[74]

permutations boded ill. A worried man, he called a council of all concerned, and put forth his fears.

"Technically," he began, "she's eligible to play for both sides, since I'm now with you and paternity has some authority in law if not in practice. And traditionally she's always played with me in this event. So I have some rights in the matter, which, however, I'm happy to concede to whoever claims her honour." I felt his eye rest on me, and felt distinctly uneasy. "But more to the point," he went on "if we don't do well in this event we may find ourselves impossibly behind in the overall standings. The Trojans have given this event full weighting, and they have most of the best women."

He paused to let his words take effect. It was true: Paris with Helen, Priam and Hecuba, Andromache with someone – there were even rumours about Aphrodite and Anchises getting together again. The best we could muster was Agamemnon with Briseis (and that meant Achilles getting the sulks again), and Odysseus with his latest Vestal Virgin – a partnership far from experienced. For a brief moment we wondered if in fact Clytemnestra shouldn't have come, then Calchas began to speak again.

"We've got one ace up the tunic," he continued. "Andromache wants to play, and with Hector now out of it she's entered with Antenor. But Antenor of the shrewd wit is technically registered with us – last year at the Academy, studying Black Holes in the Relay System, I believe – and he's forgotten to change back. So what I propose is this: we send our man to the Trojan camp" – and again his eye lighted on me – "and stake our claim to Cresseid, offering in exchange Antenor for Andromache, and if need be allowing Troilus to enter with anyone he likes (or doesn't like, for that matter). He'll be most upset, but that can only work to our advantage, and that way we'll have one half-decent pair on our side."

Which is why I found myself, under a flag of truce, graciously (at first) received by Priam, who considered the proposition I offered him. It was indeed a horny dilemma, for he would offend either Troilus or Antenor and Andromache; and with a curse upon the intricacy of the deal he muttered angrily that Calchas going over to us had certainly raised the I.Q. of both sides. There was nothing to be done but to call in Troilus and Cresseid, Antenor and Andromache, and put the situation to them.

And when Cresseid came in, I too felt the stirrings of enchantment. I had seen portraits of her, of course, as a *Virgo tintacta*, a pin-up girl, but they had done scant justice to her splendid figure. As false as

[75]

Cresseid, it had been whispered, but to me she seemed true. *"Ma che sciagura,"* I admitted quite candidly, as my eyes fell upon her and flashed her a look worth epics. She too seemed taken by me, and later I was to discover that she was recalling that magnificent grand slam, doubled and REDOUBLED, that I had made against her on my last secret visit to Troy. And so, when the decision had to be taken, Cresseid was more than willing to come with me, and despite the loud lamentations of Troilus the exchange was made. ("I was really getting a bit sick of all that true-love romance," she later confided. "The way he bills and moons like a love-struck dove.") My heart was full, I could not speak – it seemed the best of all possible worlds.

*

CANTICLE THE THIRD

The day of the Tournament soon dawned, and Cressie and I rose early to greet it. We had had but little time to work on our system, but even so the basic understanding was there – the Delphic Diamond, of course, but with Strong Two's and intricate responses over the Byzantine Four Clubs. With due ceremony we made our oblations and sacrifices to the gods, praying for glory; then made our way to the field. And so to battle, tense and tight, thrust and parry all the way, with little mercy to be given or to be expected. And now, with the last boards coming up, the outcome was far from certain. Paris and Helen had long been to the fore, but Deiphobus had replaced Paris for the final session, with scant success. We were doing well, but had yet to encounter the enraged Troilus, now playing with Cassandra, and exceeding all expectations save his own as he sought to avenge the slight which he had suffered.

Finally they arrived at our table for the last board of the match, and one that might make all the difference. Pandarus instinctively came over to kibitz, and as they took their seats Troilus hissed at Cresseid the word "Scrumpet!", and then, turning to me, hoped that I might die in poverty or of a lingering miserable disease. The perfect reply, the words of Demosthenes, sprang to my lips: "That, sir, depends on whether I embrace your system or your mistress!", but they faded in artistic frustration as I realised that the circumstances were scarcely appropriate. It was in silence, therefore, that we took out our hands:

[76]

Board 13
All Vulnerable

Cresseid
♠ —
♡ A Q J 10 4 3
◊ 7 6 5
♣ 8 5 3 2

Cassandra
♠ 4
♡ 7
◊ J 9 8 4 3 2
♣ Q J 9 6 4

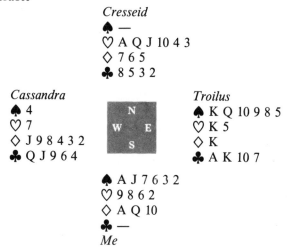

Troilus
♠ K Q 10 9 8 5
♡ K 5
◊ K
♣ A K 10 7

♠ A J 7 6 3 2
♡ 9 8 6 2
◊ A Q 10
♣ —
Me

Cresseid opened the bidding with two hearts, which I knew to be strong; hence, ignoring the double from Troilus, I immediately asked for aces with a Byzantine Four Clubs. Over the double from Cassandra Cressie passed, showing, we had agreed, one ace; but when my inquiry for kings was not doubled, she replied with five diamonds. Troilus passed, and I paused for reflection. An ace was missing, but even so seven hearts might well be on. Still, there had been that double from Troilus, so perhaps six was safer, and thus I bid the small slam only. When his turn came round Troilus inquired about the bidding, and when I explained that my partner held an ace and four kings he smiled gently and doubled viciously. With full confidence I REDOUBLED, and Cresseid turned white as a leper as the ace of clubs was led and dummy came down.

As if in a dream she played the first tricks: the ace of clubs ruffed; the ace of spades cashed; a small spade ruffed, revealing the bad split in that suit; the ace of hearts played in a vain attempt to drop the king; a diamond towards dummy, picking up that singleton king; a spade ruff; a club ruff; another spade ruff; another club ruff; and yet another spade ruff, to bring about this position, with North to lead:

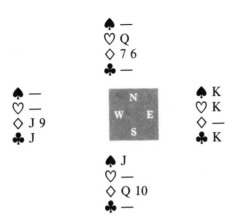

```
              ♠ —
              ♥ Q
              ♦ 7 6
              ♣ —
  ♠ —                        ♠ K
  ♥ —        N               ♥ K
  ♦ J 9    W     E           ♦ —
  ♣ J        S               ♣ K
              ♠ J
              ♥ —
              ♦ Q 10
              ♣ —
```

Cresseid now led a small diamond, and Troilus felt the agony of the unrequited squeeze. If he ruffed with the king of hearts, Cresseid would have two top tricks; if he threw the king of spades, South's jack would be good for pitching the losing diamond; while if he threw the king of clubs (which eventually he did), declarer would make her two tricks with the top diamond and a ruff of the losing spade. A neat example of elopement, which left Troilus in despair as six hearts made, REDOUBLED.

And as Cressie and I headed back in triumph to the Greek encampment, we could hear Troilus lamenting his fate and crying, "What have I done to deserve this?"; and Pandarus of the irrepressible tongue trying to console him with the sentiment that Eros by any other name is just as sore. "Lucky in cards, unlucky in love, they usually reckon," he was saying, "but the scaly hands of justice seem to have given you a pretty rough deal. But that's the way it goes. Made round to go round, so they say. Still, plenty more fish in the mackerel-crowded sea, if you know where to sling your hook." His voice was fading, but still audible. "Now, you're looking a bit down in the dumps, maybe you need a little something to pick you up, make you feel better. Well, I know this little place near the Dardanian Gate where they sell the most delicious tarts and crumpets, even buttered buns. So why don't we. . ."

XVI

The Achilles Heel (II)

Note: Achilles, the mightiest of the Greeks, had by chance seen Polyxena, youngest daughter of Priam, and, smitten by her charms, had tried to establish peace with Troy so that he might win her in marriage. While he was in the Temple of Apollo negotiating the marriage, the treacherous Paris discharged a poisoned arrow, which, guided by Apollo, mortally wounded Achilles in the heel, the only vulnerable part of his body. That Paris was a right heel is beyond all possible dispute, yet some responsibility for his fate rests in the hands of Achilles, difficult though they were. . .

For some time now the lion-hearted Achilles had been pacing about the camp in restless fury, awaiting the beginning of the Championship Pairs, in which the long-disputed rivalry between himself and tawny Paris would at last be resolved. Having earlier torn apart the Trojans in the Teams, he naturally wanted the further glory of the Pairs; but we were all aware of what underlay his wrath, and of the real reasons for his bitterness towards Paris.

Some time ago, it seems, Achilles had seen Polyxena, Priam's youngest and fairest, emerging naked from the spring, and, as Actaeon to Diana, had been staggered (as it were) by the vision of Beauty so unexpectedly revealed. And in a moment of rare romanticism he had written to her, declaring his passion and even his willingness to forsake the game forever, would she but meet him in the ambrosial night behind the Temple of Apollo. Polyxena, who has very little between the ear-rings (though plenty elsewhere), was quite willing to go, but made the mistake of showing the missive to her brother Paris, who lost little time in exploiting the affair: he reminded

Polly of Achilles's previous friendship with Patroclus, which he interpreted most ambiguously; and then made public the ambrosial assignation so that Achilles's overtures became an object of mockery in both camps ("Negotiating a naughty, as they say in the Classics" was the mildest of comments).

Finally, pouring oil on troubled flames, Paris renamed the swift-footed Achilles 'Ambrose', and stung him to the quick by bursting forth in verse which had, we were forced to admit, a perverse genius:

> Mighty Ambrose, like a God,
> Has private passions somewhat odd.
> It was because of men like this
> That Zeus made Hades bottomless.

Achilles had always hated lies and hence poetry, and the insidious power of these lines drove him to frenzy. His ears burning, he denied in vain the charges of sexual eclecticism, citing his fathering of Neoptolemus when at the court of Scyros ("But dressed as a woman," Paris taunted), and pointing to a long and honourable record of rapes and orgies as proof of his normality. To no effect: the well-aimed barb of Paris had struck Achilles's weakness, and would poison henceforth each moment of his existence.

Aware of the tension, Priam decided to exploit it to the full by arranging the draw in such a way that Achilles and Paris would meet on the final two boards. And, as if the gods approved such human ingenuity, both champions swept inexorably towards their final showdown. Achilles had been in devastating form, striking down all before him – Penthesilea, the Amazon Queen; Memnon, the dark Ethiop; even the valiant Troilus, who secretly sympathised with him. But Paris had been equally destructive, scything a swath around him – even your valiant scribe was left helplessly harrowed by another sharp ploy. At last they met, and it was clear to all that the honour and glory of the day would fall to one, and one would fall. Paris was supremely confident, greeting Achilles with "Good morrow, Ambrose", and adding for the benefit of those watching, "Once more into the Greeks, dear friends"; but Achilles, with noble disdain, ignored the mockery and simply requested the parasites to sit a little further back. The first board set the pattern of what was to follow:

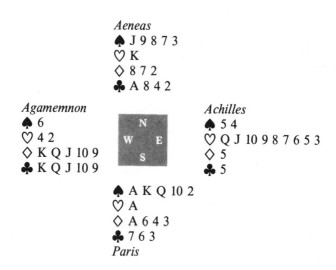

Aeneas
♠ J 9 8 7 3
♡ K
◊ 8 7 2
♣ A 8 4 2

Agamemnon
♠ 6
♡ 4 2
◊ K Q J 10 9
♣ K Q J 10 9

Achilles
♠ 5 4
♡ Q J 10 9 8 7 6 5 3
◊ 5
♣ 5

♠ A K Q 10 2
♡ A
◊ A 6 4 3
♣ 7 6 3
Paris

The bidding was simple: Paris opened one spade; Agamemnon overcalled two no trumps, guaranteeing 5–5 in the minors; Aeneas ventured three spades; Achilles had no hesitation in bidding four hearts; Paris was happy to bid four spades; and when the bidding came round to Achilles again he decided that (vulnerable) there were probably too many losers for five hearts, and reluctantly he passed. Paris played quickly: winning the opening king of clubs in dummy, he played back the 9 of spades to his ace; and then played the ace of hearts, Achilles and partner both playing low. The ace of diamonds now followed, and when Achilles did likewise Paris knew his hunch was right: Achilles had shown a singleton in each of the minors, and with a ten-card suit he would surely have competed further, so his distribution was marked. Paris therefore exited with his carefully-preserved 2 of spades to dummy's 3 and Achilles's 4; and on the forced return of a heart threw off a losing club from his hand and a diamond from dummy; and did exactly the same on the following trick. He now claimed the rest of the tricks on a cross-ruff – losing just one spade and two hearts. Typically, though, he was quick to praise the skill of Achilles in taking three tricks with such a motley collection of chariot tickets; but Achilles, aware that he should have kept his 3 of hearts as an exit, said nothing, and Agamemnon's face remained a mask.

All now depended on the final board. Aeneas opened a Delphic Diamond, but despite an overcall of one no trump from Achilles (16–18 points), Paris again bought the contract in four spades:

[81]

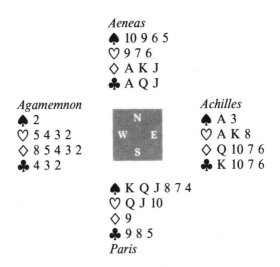

Aeneas
♠ 10 9 6 5
♡ 9 7 6
♦ A K J
♣ A Q J

Agamemnon
♠ 2
♡ 5 4 3 2
♦ 8 5 4 3 2
♣ 4 3 2

Achilles
♠ A 3
♡ A K 8
♦ Q 10 7 6
♣ K 10 7 6

♠ K Q J 8 7 4
♡ Q J 10
♦ 9
♣ 9 8 5
Paris

Agamemnon sparked off with a diamond, which Paris won in dummy with the ace. He now exited with a spade, whereupon Achilles cashed the ace of spades and two heart tricks; then exited with a trump and sat back to wait for his fourth trick in the minors. Paris, however, looked supremely unconcerned. He immediately played the 9 of clubs to dummy's ace, not even pausing to think of the finesse; then played off another trump and his last heart, Agamemnon carefully showing that he had all the 2's and most of the 3's. Then on the fifth trump the Grecian commander discarded his last heart, dummy the jack of clubs, and Achilles a club, to bring about a position ideally suited to the Trojan Coup:

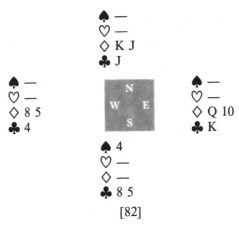

♠ —
♡ —
♦ K J
♣ J

♠ —
♡ —
♦ 8 5
♣ 4

♠ —
♡ —
♦ Q 10
♣ K

♠ 4
♡ —
♦ —
♣ 8 5

When Paris played the last trump, Agamemnon threw a small diamond, and dummy its last club, leaving Achilles to ponder the whereabouts of the 8 and 5 of clubs. Caught in two minds, he finally made up the wrong one and threw the king of clubs (on the not unreasonable supposition that his partner might have clubs, as both Paris's refusal to finesse the clubs and his failure to cash the top diamond had suggested). But again he was left wearing the ass's ears, as an exultant Paris cashed the 8 and 5 of clubs to win the championship on a pseudo-sqeeze against the mighty Achilles. ("The only possible way," he told all who would listen later, "with all the points off-side, and the initial diamond lead messing up my communications for a Vienna Coup and genuine squeeze.")

With a face like thunder Achilles stomped to his feet and took to his heels, disappearing into the ambrosial night. And when we returned to the camp some hours later, it was to find his tents gone and the stern of his black ship disappearing over the moon-lit horizon. This was indeed a blow to our hopes, for without the mighty Achilles our chances of ultimate victory were severely reduced. We held a hasty post-mortem, and Agamemnon led the public mourning ("If you have ears, prepare to shed them now"), but even Odysseus was moved to comment. "I don't like it at all," he muttered. "It's all very well Agamemnon saying that Paris wears his helmet to hide his circumcision scar, but there's no concealing the damage he's done. He's a great player, mind you, and those were two great coups, but they've cut back our chances completely. What a pain he is – I don't so much object to his always having an extra trump up his tunic as to his total conviction that Apollo puts it there for him – with an ego like that, it's a wonder his head fits through the door. Something's got to be done about him, and quickly, before he strikes again, for it's obvious to everybody that we're in great trouble, now that the lion-hearted Achilles has been brought down in his pride."

XVII

The Agony of Ajax

Note: After the death of Achilles, the Greeks were ordered by the gods to bestow his sumptuous armour (that fashioned by Hephaestus) upon the most deserving of heroes. The prize was claimed by both Ajax and Odysseus, but a select committee of Grecian leaders awarded it to the latter, thus placing wisdom before valour. According to one tradition, Ajax, filled with chagrin at this decision, fell upon his sword; and on the spot where his blood sank into the ground a hyacinth sprang up, marked with the letters 'AI', the Greek for "woe". Another story, however, recounts that Ajax, driven insane by rage and disappointment, turned on the captured livestock, and, mistaking them for the men of Odysseus, slew them furiously before killing himself. Given the existence of such divergent accounts, it is the more imperative that we here set forth the true version of that fateful tragedy. . .

The resentment of Ajax towards Odysseus had long been smouldering, especially since the Games when Odysseus had laid claim to the Vestal Virgin, leaving him with the Tripod; and it flickered into flame when Achilles's lucky mascot Zeno was found amidst the rubbish which mighty Achilles had left behind. Odysseus, with a cry of hungry triumph, had proposed its metamorphosis into soup; but Ajax, who couldn't bear to hurt a lamb, had opposed him strongly, and claimed bronze-backed Zeno for his own (a Daphne-substitute, some of us felt). The matter was as yet unresolved, but the contempt of Ajax for Odysseus had been marked from that moment on. Yet in calling Odysseus an animal Ajax surely went too far, for the proud son of Laertes would accept such abuse from no man; and when it came to a battle of wits and insults, the polytropic Odysseus was more than a match for elephant Ajax.

Time passed (having no alternative), and the feeling between them grew worse. Ajax further insulted Odysseus by saying that he'd wring his neck, if he'd only wash it first; and Odysseus, as much surprised as offended by a bite from such a lamb, in turn accused great Ajax of being a sheep in sheep's clothing, and of having a mind as barren as the banks of Libya. He furthermore concocted what he called the

'AI' test ("Artificial Idiocy," he explained, "or the Aberration Index – a measure of the woeful level of the Ajax intellect.") Some typical questions were:

1. Why do Ajax's cows wear bells?
   a. To ring in the gnu
   b. Because their horns don't work.
2. What has four legs and flies?
   a. A dead horse
   b. Pegasus.
3. What is worse than Ajax finding a worm in his apple?
   a. Two worms
   b. Half a worm.
4. When is Ajax like the Parthenon?
   a. When he is per-Phidias
   b. When he loses his marbles.

Ajax didn't find it in the least amusing, but the craze for Ajax Iokes quickly caught on. Some of us thought Odysseus had gone a bit too far, especially with No. 4, but with a curt "No brain, no pain" Odysseus refused to apologize, and reasserted his claim to Zeno.

Matters came to a head with the selection of the Knockout Teams. Agamemnon and Menelaus, by right of might if not of playing strength, were automatically in the top team, and it had been more or less assumed that Odysseus and I would be selected with them. Ajax, however, had different ideas. He put forward the claim of himself and young Aias, arguing that their right to play was as good as ours, and demanding the chance to prove it. Odysseus, surprisingly, had no objections. "Great Ajax and Lesser Aias," he explained to me, "are two buttocks of one bum, and it's about time somebody put them in their place and pulled the chain. Besides, it's time this Zeno paradox was resolved, once and for all. And even if we do lose, so what? It's no great shakes (as the Vestal Virgin said to the Bard) 'pearing on the same team as Menelaus."

Thus the challenge was accepted and got under way: thirteen boards to be played; Agamemnon, Menelaus and Calchas to scrutinise the results; and Zeno to be placed on the table midway between Odysseus and Ajax so that his luck should be distributed equally. It proved to be a needle match in every respect, with Odysseus losing no opportunity to scratch a prickly Ajax; and with twelve boards gone the result seemed in the balance. It was with some trepidation, therefore, that we picked up our last hands:

[85]

Board 13
All Vulnerable

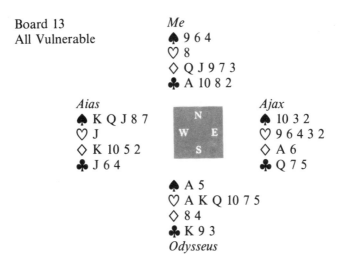

Me
♠ 9 6 4
♡ 8
◇ Q J 9 7 3
♣ A 10 8 2

Aias
♠ K Q J 8 7
♡ J
◇ K 10 5 2
♣ J 6 4

Ajax
♠ 10 3 2
♡ 9 6 4 3 2
◇ A 6
♣ Q 7 5

♠ A 5
♡ A K Q 10 7 5
◇ 8 4
♣ K 9 3
Odysseus

I passed (having no alternative), and Ajax did the same. Odysseus opened up with an Offensive Club, and, despite a spade overcall from Aias, bullied his way to four hearts, which Ajax promptly doubled, hoping to put Odysseus in his place. Aias led the king of spades, which Odysseus ducked; though he had to win the queen which followed. Three rounds of trumps now followed, Aias discarding two spades. Still looking at a potential five losers altogether, Odysseus led a diamond, which Aias won with the king. Playing safe (he thought), he came back another spade, which Odysseus ruffed. Another diamond then lost to Ajax's ace, to leave the following position, with Odysseus needing every trick:

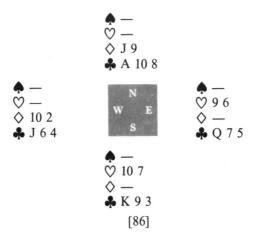

♠ —
♡ —
◇ J 9
♣ A 10 8

♠ —
♡ —
◇ 10 2
♣ J 6 4

♠ —
♡ 9 6
◇ —
♣ Q 7 5

♠ —
♡ 10 7
◇ —
♣ K 9 3

[86]

Ajax was now in trouble. He could not lead a heart, but his choice of the club 7 proved equally woeful when Odysseus covered with the 9, forcing the jack and ace. Dummy's 10 of clubs now followed, and Ajax felt the agony: if he were to cover with the queen, the 8 in dummy would be an entry to the diamonds for a trump coup; and if he didn't cover (he didn't) Odysseus would play the 3 from his own hand, then switch to the jack of diamonds – if Ajax were to ruff that, then Odysseus would over-ruff, and his hand would be high; and if he were to discard his club (he did), Odysseus would do likewise, and then play the last club from the table, again generating the trump coup, and compressing five losers into three. Like a bad Ajax Ioke, there were always two lines of response, and Ajax was impaled upon either.

Once again, Ajax was not amused. He glared at Aias, wanting to know why he had come back that third spade, allowing Odysseus to shorten his trumps like that; but Aias, highly indignant, retorted to the effect that Ajax of all people could ill-afford to give anybody a piece of his mind. Odysseus, standing by the door, chuckled loudly at the insult, at which Ajax finally saw red: he picked up Zeno, spun round furiously, and hurled him like a discus at Odysseus, who ducked just in time to see poor Zeno, moving faster than ever in his life (even Achilles couldn't have caught him), twinkling like a meteor across the dusky plain.

Well, if the record set by Hyacinth was shattered, so was Zeno. And so too was Ajax when he realised what he had done. In tearful contrition he stumbled from the tent, vowing to give up the game forever, to put an end to it all. Some of us thought he meant it quite seriously, and were rather worried, but Odysseus was unrepentant. "Suicide," he scoffed, as we sat round later sipping turtle soup. "That's the last thing he'd ever do. No, serve him right, as far as I'm concerned. Great oafs from little infants grow, they say, but that last fling of his almost felled me. If great Ajax wants to take my place in the team, he's got to stop throwing his weight around like that."

XVIII

Philoctetes Misses a Trick

Note: Philoctetes, son of Poeas, had lit the pines of Heracles's funeral
pyre, and had inherited the latter's great bow; but on his way to
Troy had been bitten on the foot by a water-serpent (some say,
wounded by one of his own arrows). The stench of his
unhealing wound making him an object of distress to his fellow
Greeks, he had been marooned on the island of Lemnos. Ten
years lapsed, and the Greeks discovered that Troy would not
fall until Neoptolemus, son of Achilles, came into the attack,
and Philoctetes with his great bow was brought back from
Lemnos. Diomedes, Odysseus and Neoptolemus were dispatched to fetch the reluctant archer (who had little reason to
trust the first two), and by trickery they were able to take
away his bow and compel him to come to Troy. There were
many cross words, however, when the full duplicity of
Odysseus was revealed. . .

He was the long-haired artistic type, was Philoctetes, full of idiotic
complexes about suffering and genius, super-egotistic, and never
washing (old "flock of fleas" we called him). And on the way to Troy
he'd got his toga in a tangle about something, and, pleading a touch
of catharsis, had stopped off at Lemnos for a while. Truth to tell, we
didn't mind too much. "Bad breath is better than none," he'd say, but
we weren't so sure. Anyway, he'd been on the island for the duration,
fooling around with his clam-digger, taking potshots at any passing
albatross, and making up complicated puzzles and hands for his own
dirty delight. He also fancied himself as a poet, they reckoned:

> I'm glad I use Sunlight, the octopus said,
> Or else with eight armpits I'd rather be dead.

That kind of thing. But now with swift-footed Achilles put out of the
running by the devious ALEXANDROS (to give Paris his proper
name), champion archer of Troy, we needed something to combat the
Belligerent Club wielded by the Trojans, and Philoctetes alone knew
the Heraclean variations of the Offensive Club.

Neoptolemus, newly arrived in place of his father, was anxious to
prove himself a chip off the old marble, and had volunteered for the

task of persuading Philoctetes to come to Troy. There were murmurs at this, for we all knew Philoctetes could run rings round him, but, surprisingly, Odysseus was all for it. Philoctetes would not trust the rest of us, he argued, but he might just underestimate the likely lad if it came to a battle of wits. On the way to Lemnos, therefore, Odysseus coached Ptolly in the format and ritual of the three-round challenge, giving him a run-down of the traditional questions and likely variants, and setting up a Chi-word puzzle should the contest go to the decider.

We landed darkly at dead of night, and carefully made our way to the rocky promontory where Philoctetes dwelt. Odysseus and I took up our positions behind the rocks, while Neoptolemus sat crossed-legged before the mouth of the cave until the rosy fingers of dawn lit the funereal pines. He then called into the cave in ritual manner, challenging Philoctetes to oracular exchange, the winner for thirteen moons to be slave and helot to the other. Bleary and unwashed, Philoctetes stumbled from his cave clutching his great bow in his grimy paws, but seeing it was only Neoptolemus (and being tired of opening his own clams) accepted the challenge without hesitation.

The first round was easy. In deference to Oedipal tradition, Philoctetes was required to ask something of the four-legs, three-legs, two-legs kind, and he trotted out the old one, almost contemptuously: two-legs put one-leg on three-legs; in came four-legs, picked up one-legs, and ran away; two-legs picked up three-legs, threw it at four-legs, who dropped one-leg, etc. Neoptolemus had no difficulty in identifying the dog, the priest, the tripod, and the sacrificial offering. In return, he asked Philoctetes what a man does standing up, a woman sitting down, and a dog with one leg raised. Philoctetes was not in the least troubled: "Shake hands," he retorted; and immediately asked what was the difference between a battle-horse and a baker's horse. That was one we'd expected, and Neoptolemus knew the answer: "A battle-horse darts into the fray," he replied; and immediately came back with, "What's the difference (no insult intended) between a lousy archer and a constipated owl?" Philoctetes was stuck for a moment, but finally worked it out that a lousy archer shoots and shoots and never hits. His final question was one we'd overlooked: "What's a Grecian urn?" We were afraid that Ptolly would come up with the obvious "forty drachmas", but we too had underestimated the lad: "What he's ode!" came the triumphant reply. But his last question was rather feeble: "What do you give a Greek who has everything?"; and Philoctetes had no trouble finding the

[89]

answer: "More!"

It was stalemate, which meant that each contestant now had to give the other a logical labyrinth to thread his way through. Neoptolemus therefore produced the Chi-word which Odysseus had composed, and gave it to Philoctetes, retaining the sealed answer. Attic rules (rather than Ionic) were to prevail, with 'ph' and 'ps' to count as a single letter and, of course, all non-classical barbarisms excluded. Philoctetes took one look at the first clue, and with a muttered "Huh, that's me!", set to work:

Across

1. Champion archer.
8. The intimate self.
9. Half of Dora would be all right.
10. Of major significance.
11. – up, and keep out of sight.
13. A language of Greece.
14. To request.
15. A decoration.
17. Circe at home?
18. May be wriggled.
20. The source of energy.
23. Deceptive scare? Should be taken.
26. A place of rest.
28. The one-eyed king?
29. In the positive mode.

Down

2. Score deviously?
3. Thin fare? Not if made right.
4. The poetic type.
5. Towards sunrise.
6. To give knowledge for the future.
7. One who is too full of liquid?
10. One who is forced to work unpaid.
12. To bring to tears?
16. Having a seedy and deserted look.
19. A royal appointment?
21. Better suited to a load than an ode.
22. Zeus's bird?
24. In a sorry state.
25. Slothful act.
27. Unusual river.

Neoptolemus, meanwhile, was agonising over a set of Kryptic Xrostics, pulled from the depths of Philoctetes's mothy pockets:

#		Clue
1.	- - - - -	Pairs Champion of Troy.
2.	- - - - - - - - -	Workers in the ship have strength, but fall in love.
3.	- - - - - - - - - - - - - - - - -	Vestal Virgin saves her honour and defeats the contract.
4.	- - - - - - - - -	Not played; hence the Embankment; hence played.
5.	- - - - - - -	So clear, but so ambiguous.
6.	- - - - - - - - - -	No bloomers, but nevertheless behind.
7.	- - - - -	A deceptive play.
8.	- - - - - - - - - - -	Stripped, and I'm in elation.
9.	- - - - - - - - - - - -	Offer to take over? On the contrary – the contract is not wanted.
10.	- - - -	Responds to Psyche and gets sore.
11.	- - - - - - - - - - -	Has never set – a grand contract.
12.	- - - - - - - - - - - - -	Deeper than deep? Not necessarily, but must be taken both ways.
13.	- - - - - - - - - - - -	Queer sets zip to turn an extra trick.
14.	- - - - - - - - -	Hera? Athena? No, but the pair do confuse Paris.
15.	- - - - -	Change partners for up and down results?
16.	- - - - - - - - - - - -	Helpless tone? Paris carries her off.
17.	- - - - - - - - - - - - - - - - - - -	Here is a pacific sign I turned that the gods might bring the winds.
18.	- - - - - - - - - - -	They sit on a thorn and shout?
19.	- - - - - - - - - - - - -	If no smoking Dad, it's a one-eyed rule.
20.	- - - - - - - -	Last rites?
21.	- - - - - - - - - - - - - - - -	No option, hot critics decree.

From our point of vantage we watched Philoctetes nonchalantly scratching his dandruff as he filled out the answers. Only at the very end did he look puzzled, but with a shrug wrote in the final letters and sat back to look at Neoptolemus still struggling over his clues. As the sands ran out we could see that Ptolly was far from finished, and in despair I looked at Odysseus who, for some reason, seemed equally well composed. When the time was up they exchanged answers, those of Neoptolemus contemptuously completed by Philoctetes:

1. Paris. 2. Hold Hands.   3. Immaculate Defence.
4. Last Trump.   5. Oracles.   6. Cold Bottom.   7. Trick.
8. Elimination.   9. Transfer Bid.   10. Eros.
11. Seven Hearts.   12. Intra-Finesse.   13. Strip Squeeze.
14. Aphrodite.   15. Swing.   16. Topless Helen.
17. Iphigenia's Sacrifice.   18. North-South.
19. King of Diamonds.   20. End-Play.   21. Restricted Choice.

"Yours wasn't much of a puzzle," said Philoctetes disdainfully, licking his lips at the thought of a year's free clams. "'Diamond' should really be 'Diamonds', and sloth is a sin – not the other way round. And as for 'od' and 'da' – trans-Cimmerian references like that are a bit beyond the pale. And isn't it supposed to be 'ob'? As a setter of Chi-words you'll make a much better clam-digger."

"It wasn't my fault," burst out Neoptolemus, perilously close to tears. "Odysseus set it up, and me likewise."

"Odysseus!" Philoctetes turned leprous-white, and grabbed at the puzzle. A muffled groan escaped his lips as he looked again at the clues, and at what he'd put down. He reached frantically for the sealed answer still held by Neptolemus, but before he could get it Odysseus stepped forth from behind the rocks. Philoctetes subsided, and before he could recover I crept up behind and seized the great bow.

However, there was no resistance. Philoctetes quietly packed up his few horrid objects, put them on his shoulder, and followed us to the shore. Without complaint he even washed and oiled himself before calmly taking his seat in the bow. And as we scudded Troywards over the blue Aegean I marvelled to Odysseus that he had come so quietly, especially since he had won the contest.

"Won the contest?" scoffed Odysseus. "What in Hades do you mean? He didn't get a single right answer, and he's hoping that if he doesn't make a fuss I won't tell anybody how big a fool he was."

Ptolly and I still didn't get it, so Odysseus, with a look a derision, broke the waxen seal and pulled out the answers:

```
A  L  E  X  A  N  D  R  O  S
·  I  D  ·  R  A  ·  R  A  ·
H  E  A  R  T  ·  W  R  A  P
E  ·  M  ·  I  O  N  I  C  ·
L  ·  ·  ·  S  ·  ·  P  L  Y
O  M  ·  S  T  Y  ·  ·  E  ·
T  O  E  ·  I  ·  M  A  S  S
·  T  R  I  C  K  ·  S  ·  W
·  H  ·  L  ·  I  ·  S  P  A
C  Y  C  L  O  P  S  ·  O  N
```

"He didn't do too badly," I said rather feebly, but Odysseus just snorted, and said something about Art with a capital F. And as the island of Lemnos sank slowly into the purpled west, Ptolly and I looked at each other significantly. Perhaps Philoctetes was not, after all, the greasiest of the Greeks. That preference/reference to Paris Alexandros had obviously hurt, and we could see now why he felt so wounded. Privately we felt a bit sorry for him. Philoctetes is a stinker, we agreed, but that kind of thing also leaves a bad smell.

[93]

XIX

Paris Plays the Last Trump

Note: Philoctetes, champion archer of the Greeks, had been brought
back from Lemnos, and his wound was healed by Machaon,
the healer. He now entered into battle, and immediately struck
Paris with one of the poisoned arrows bequeathed to him by
Heracles. Mortally wounded, Paris was taken to Mount Ida to
seek the nymph Oenone who alone could cure him. But
Oenone, recalling the wrongs she had suffered (when Paris
abandoned her for Helen), refused to heal the wound, and
Paris returned to Troy to die. Oenone repented, but too late,
and finding Paris dead hanged herself in her grief. This latter
tale of tragic love has received attention from poets such as
Tennyson and William Morris, but, strangely, few previous
writers have considered the equally harrowing drama of the
earlier confrontation between Philoctetes and Paris. . .

Time's arrow had moved inexorably on, and only the Knockout
Teams remained to be contested – the Pankration, it was called, for
there would be no holds barred and few of the niceties observed. The
draw had been made, and it was with some relief that Odysseus and I
found ourselves at the other end of the field, out of the immediate
range of tawny Paris, who, fresh from his triumph over Achilles in the
Pairs, was looking to put new notches on his ivory-and-ibex-horn
scorecard ("Arrogance I can take," muttered Odysseus in disgust,
"but whoever heard of strutting around in a panther skin? There but
for the grace of Zeus goes Zeus. It really is obscene.")

Still, we had less to worry about than Philoctetes and Neoptolemus,
who were up against Paris in the very first round. They were lying
down, disconsolate, and in vain did Agamemnon, King of lyric
heros, give his usual rousing speech – the don't-die-for-your-
country-let-the-poor-bastard-on-the-other-side-die-for-his one – and
in vain did he consult the Oracle, only to get this garbled message:

Time flies like an arrow
An arrow winking O fly rich Eros
There as on Ida rise afresh win
Disgusting you rest at ease verse cures
O the best of all sofa destroy

[94]

"What a load of old gobblers," I muttered in musophobic vein. "I know poetry isn't meant to make sense, and it's obviously got something to do with archer Paris rising to victory from his couch of love lest worse him befall, but for my money 'cures' should be 'obscures'. And what about 'sofa' – it doesn't even make grammatical sense, unless it's one of those funny Greek plurals ending in 'a' – any old stigma to beat a dogma with. And as for 'Time flies like an arrow' – you might as well say 'Fruit flies like a banana'."

"That's it," Odysseus suddenly broke in. "You've got it exactly." But before I could ask what I'd got exactly he'd pulled Philoctetes aside and was whispering something in his ear. Funny how well those two get on now – they're two of a kind, really – brilliant but. . . Still, Philoctetes certainly looked a lot happier, and it was with some animation now that he was listening to Odysscus's final advice.

"Don't forget," Odysseus concluded. "If pigs could fly, Paris would be your fully-fledged swine. He's a real vulture, and he'll be out to gyp you if he can. Remember, they may be playing Etruscan Asking Bids – the feet under the table kind – and watch out for those left-handed leads – they're more sinister than gauche. In other words, don't trust Paris an inch – if he looks in your hand, make sure you count your points afterwards."

As they disappeared I remarked to Odysseus that that was the last we'd be seeing of them. But Odysseus grinned mysteriously, and told me not to count my points before they were dealt. "There's no flies on Philoctetes," he said. "Figuratively speaking that is. He knows a trick or two, and if he can pull one off against the Trojans Paris will be determined to get it back with interest. They're two of a kind, really – brilliant but corrupt, like mackerel in the moonlight that shines and stinks. Vultures, the pair of them. Besides, we've got a couple of things going for us – Oenone's on the Appeals Committee, and she won't be taking any nonsense from Paris after what happened during that earlier session on Mount Ida. And don't forget the Oracle, which you interpreted so well." He clapped me on the shoulder, but before I could ask what he meant he was off to see the action.

There were to be twenty-six hands in all, Philoctetes and Neoptolemus against Paris and Antenor – described by Agamemnon as greasy and crude against oily and refined. But over the first dozen

[95]

boards Odysseus's confidence seemed to be well-placed, for Phlox and Ptolly were playing with some assurance, and weren't far behind when Board 13 hit the table:

Board 13
All Vulnerable

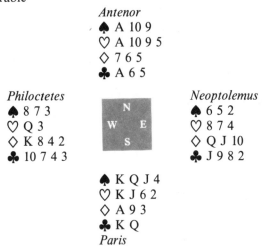

Antenor
♠ A 10 9
♡ A 10 9 5
◇ 7 6 5
♣ A 6 5

Philoctetes
♠ 8 7 3
♡ Q 3
◇ K 8 4 2
♣ 10 7 4 3

Neoptolemus
♠ 6 5 2
♡ 8 7 4
◇ Q J 10
♣ J 9 8 2

♠ K Q J 4
♡ K J 6 2
◇ A 9 3
♣ K Q
Paris

There was no hesitation in the bidding, Paris quickly shooting to six hearts. Philoctetes led a neutral club, which Paris won in hand. His only worry was the heart queen, and, faced with the two-way Janus finesse, Paris decided to improve his chances by first "running" the jack of spades, as if looking for the queen. When Philoctetes flickered, Paris went up with the ace, and came back to hand with the king of clubs. He then led the jack of hearts; again Philoctetes flickered; so Paris, not to be fooled, climbed with the ace and ran the ten back. When it lost to the queen he was livid, for a diamond still had to be conceded; but he could hardly appeal against a hesitation which actually showed the card he was looking for, so there was little he could do beyond swear vengeance for later. And thus at the half Philoctetes and Neoptolemus found themselves narrowly winning, thanks to the big swing picked up on this board.

The second half began with some rancour, but slowly Paris and Antenor started to get back the deficit. Even so, there was very little in it, and this fact, as well as wounded pride, prompted Paris to aim high on the very last board:

[96]

Board 26
All Vulnerable

Antenor
♠ 9 6 3
♡ A K 9 2
◇ A 10 3 2
♣ Q 7

Philoctetes
♠ Q 2
♡ 7 6 5 3
◇ K Q J 9
♣ 9 6 5

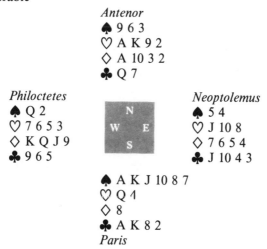

Neoptolemus
♠ 5 4
♡ J 10 8
◇ 7 6 5 4
♣ J 10 4 3

♠ A K J 10 8 7
♡ Q 4
◇ 8
♣ A K 8 2
Paris

At the other table (it later transpired) there had been a total mix-up in the bidding, and Aias as North had somehow ended up in a horrible five diamonds, which made when East failed to find the trump lead: three club tricks; two spade tricks; three heart tricks, ending in hand; the last heart led and ruffed with the 8 of diamonds; then the ace–10 of diamonds at the end. Even so, Aias wasn't happy as they had missed the Grand in spades – with only four trumps missing, Paris would surely play for the drop, wouldn't he? And even bidding six (or perhaps four) would be enough.

Sure enough, Paris bid the Grand, and Philoctetes led Old Cyclops. Paris won in hand; then played the ace of trumps, dropping the 2, 3 and 4. His natural play was now the king, but, still furious with Philoctetes, he saw a way of protecting himself should there be three spades including the queen onside – the infamous Albatross Coup. Accordingly, he crossed to dummy with a club; and led the 9 of spades, noting the 5 from East, and casually playing the 8 of clubs from his own hand. Before Antenor could inquire politely, "No trumps, partner?", Philoctetes had discarded a heart; and Paris, trying to look as honest as he could (but now knowing East to have the queen), substituted the 8 of spades. He was about to claim the rest of the tricks when to his horror he saw Philoctetes replace his small heart with the queen of trumps ("I didn't spend all that time on the island for nothing," he later stated modestly, when we marvelled at his defence to the coup).

There was no doubt about it: Paris was shafted, and eliminated from further action. He prolonged the agony by calling for the director, but Peisistratus was adamant that Philoctetes could change his card without penalty, and though Paris tried to appeal for a revoke, Oenone refused to salve his wounded pride ("She'll regret it," he muttered). With bad grace, therefore, Paris made his painful exit, to our unrestrained jubilation and perhaps even the secret delight of the Trojans, to whom he had become an object of distaste as much as of admiration ("As popular as a turd in the wine bowl," Antenor was later to admit, in an uncharacteristic breach of decorum).

Our celebrations continued long into the night, with Philoctetes the toast of us all. Odysseus, however, was looking slightly put out, and at last I realised that nobody was appreciating *his* desperate attempts to look modest. But since a player's first duty is to his partner, I finally took pity upon him, and asked him to tell all.

"I don't want to take all the credit," he began, "for after all it was Philoctetes who pulled out that old chestnut and roasted Paris, and I don't want to take that away from him. But *I* was the one who interpreted what the Oracle meant, and thereby gave him the confidence to get up and face Paris." We looked at him quizzically, and, feigning reluctance, Odysseus spelt out what the Oracle had really said to Agamemnon:

> *Time flies like an arrow*
> *A narrow win king of lyric heros*
> *The reason I'd arise a fresh wind is gusting*
> *Your estate as ever secure*
> *So Thebes to fall so fades Troy*

"You must admit," he concluded rather jealously, "that I had some part to play, humble though it be. It was a cultured coup, and one that caught Paris on the wing, but sometimes I feel a bit like Prometheus – when I hear the word 'vulture' I reach for my cross-bow. I'm glad Paris isn't hanging round our necks any more, but you mustn't give Philoctetes too much praise – it was a bit of a long shot, and he's really rather lucky that it came off as well as it did."

XX

The Wooden Bunny

Note: After ten years, and despite the death of Paris, the Trojans were still holding out, and the Greeks, beginning to despair of ever subjugating them by force, resorted instead to strategem. On the advice of Odysseus, and with the help of Athena, they constructed a wooden horse of mountainous bulk, its ribs interwoven with planks of fir, and filled it with chosen heroes; the remainder of the Greek forces taking to the ships and retreating beyond the island of Tenedos. The outcome of this rare device will form the substance of our later tales; but we must first consider how Odysseus was able to persuade his fellow Greeks that such a desperate undertaking might meet with success, and how the heroes for the enterprise were chosen. . .

It was an impasse: taking the elimination of their top team badly, the Trojans had retreated into the citadel and were refusing us admittance, indefinitely delaying the start of the next round, and jeering at us when we demanded the right of entry: "Grecians, withdraw, like your fathers should have done." For what seemed like years we waited, and at last the bold Odysseus was moved to call a council to decide what should be done.

"It's no good," he declared. "They've got us over a barrel, as Diogenes would say. Either we get fed up and go home, in which case they win by default; or else we lose so many points for being late that it's hardly worth fighting anyway. The rules simply state that we've got to be in the Pergamon Room tomorrow evening to field a team, but there's nothing in them that specifically forces the Trojans to unlock the gates. So we've got to get in, and therein lies the problem."

He paused, and looked round at the gloomy assembly. What he had said was true enough: wingless victory though it might seem by using such means, victory nevertheless it would be.

"I know," said young Aias at last. "We'll dig a tunnel and come up underneath them – they won't see what we're up to because we'll be pretending to run and vault. I read all about it in a chronicle somewhere – I forget what it was called." Our gloom became even more profound, and even Aias saw how out of character it would be for out of form heroes to run and vault, to say nothing of digging – we would only raise clouds of dust as we tried to cover our tracks ("Just

[99]

because I call a spade a spade," muttered Agamemnon, "it doesn't mean to say I want to use one").

Noting the silence, Odysseus clicked his fingers decisively. "There's only one thing for it," he declared. "It's got to be something completely original, something so innovative that they'd never suspect it. In other words, the Wooden Bunny." We looked at him incredulously as he went on to explain that the one thing the Trojans couldn't resist was a gift. "Especially," he added, "if they think we've all gone home and left them a votive offering as a tribute to their victory. And after all, it's Easter, so what could be more natural?" So we were to cut down some tall arrowy white pines, and make of them a large firry beast, with room inside it for a handful of heroes (and, in case they felt like peeking, a sign on the outside saying 'Not To Be Opened Until Easter'). The idea was that they'd be taken into the city, whereupon they could leap out and demand the right to play, holding the fort (as it were) till the rest of us got there.

Some of us were a bit dubious (Menelaus in particular saying that he'd be the last to get into such a beast), but nobody could think of a better idea, so we finally agreed to give it a try. So Epeus and the boys set to work on the animal, while Odysseus directed himself to the selection of heroes. He would go, he declared, and since everybody else obviously would want to as well, there would have to be a series of eliminations – an extermination of bunnies, as he called it.

Sad to relate, your humble scribe was caught in the carrot-patch and weeded out on the very first hand. As Odysseus put it to us, you were South, and the contract (for reasons best known to your partner) was four hearts, with the ace of spades lead followed by another.

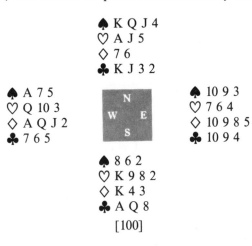

♠ K Q J 4
♡ A J 5
♢ 7 6
♣ K J 3 2

♠ A 7 5   ♠ 10 9 3
♡ Q 10 3   ♡ 7 6 4
♢ A Q J 2   ♢ 10 9 8 5
♣ 7 6 5   ♣ 10 9 4

♠ 8 6 2
♡ K 9 8 2
♢ K 4 3
♣ A Q 8

Like most of the bunnies, I won the second spade; crossed back to hand with a club; and finessed the heart. When everything behaved I had eleven tricks, for what I thought must surely be a good result. Unlucky! The point of the hand, Odysseus later explained, was to eliminate the simple-minded finessers, and anybody making eleven tricks was out. Top marks, paradoxically, went to those who cashed the ace of hearts at trick 3; then ran the jack, losing to the queen; won the return in dummy; and played another heart to the 9, losing to the 10 for one down – the point was not to risk losing a trick to the dangerous hand. The actual result, he pointed out, was unimportant – what mattered was the principle. Menelaus, however, passed the test in a different manner: he cashed a third spade, three clubs, and the top two hearts before exiting with a heart to endplay West in diamonds – and since the Oracle had not foreseen such a stupid but successful line of play, he was allowed to continue, much to his disgust.

And to his surprise, as well as that of Odysseus, Menelaus was still in contention when the Oracle issued the thirteenth and final hand; and both of them were determined that he wouldn't succeed this time:

Board 13
All Vulnerable

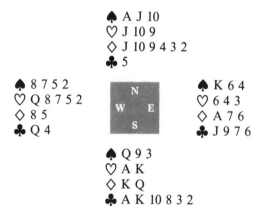

```
                    ♠ A J 10
                    ♡ J 10 9
                    ◇ J 10 9 4 3 2
                    ♣ 5
    ♠ 8 7 5 2              N              ♠ K 6 4
    ♡ Q 8 7 5 2        W       E          ♡ 6 4 3
    ◇ 8 5                  S              ◇ A 7 6
    ♣ Q 4                                 ♣ J 9 7 6
                    ♠ Q 9 3
                    ♡ A K
                    ◇ K Q
                    ♣ A K 10 8 3 2
```

This time the contract was three no trumps, and the lead the 5 of hearts. Even Menelaus (looking at only his hand and dummy) could see that the fate of the contract depended on the whereabouts of the king of spades, for if it were off-side West's hearts would be set up before the diamonds could be enjoyed. Determined to go down,

Menelaus resolved to give destiny a nudge, just in case the king of spades was on-side. He therefore won the king of hearts; played off his king and queen of diamonds, East holding off; then overtook his queen of spades with the ace – that should guarantee defeat, he thought, but just to make it absolutely certain he decided to get rid of his winning ace of hearts on the third diamond. He did so, and it was only when the defence won and continued with hearts that Menelaus realised that he had unwittingly perpetrated an act of brilliancy – the jack–10 in dummy was now an entry to all the established diamonds. Worse was to follow: as Menelaus reluctantly accepted his Fate and ran the diamonds, he was able to create this position:

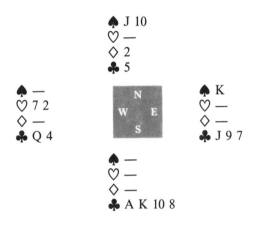

```
                  ♠ J 10
                  ♡ —
                  ◇ 2
                  ♣ 5

   ♠ —                          ♠ K
   ♡ 7 2          N             ♡ —
   ◇ —        W       E         ◇ —
   ♣ Q 4          S             ♣ J 9 7

                  ♠ —
                  ♡ —
                  ◇ —
                  ♣ A K 10 8
```

On the last diamond East was inevitably squeezed, and when the dust had cleared Menelaus had made five no trumps, while most were going down in three. With some reluctance, Odysseus was forced to award him the Brilliancy Nimbus, and with even greater reluctance Menelaus was forced to accept it and take his place among the elite group of heroes inside the Wooden Bunny.

"It's going to be a tight squeeze," he muttered, as, last to get into the beast, he gazed up into the cramped confines. "And it's all very well to talk about unblocking – but decapitation will be the least of our headaches if the Trojans look this gift horse in the mouth. It's not my idea of a good time, you know, but what choice did I have? Some are born to greatness, they say, and others achieve greatness, and I know that destiny once dealt can't really be revoked – but I sometimes wish the gods hadn't chosen me to thrust greatness upon."

XXI

The Serpent Coup

Note: The Greeks had sailed away, leaving behind the Wooden Horse; and in the morning the Trojans swarmed from their city like bees to behold the marvel. Opinion was divided as to whether or not it should be taken within the walls, and Laocoön, Priest of Poseidon, threw his lance at the horse and warned his countymen against accepting the gift (*"Timeo Danaos et dona ferentes"* – I fear the Greeks, even when bearing gifts). The Trojans might have taken his advice, but for two things: first, a Greek named Sinon had been captured (left behind through the treachery of Odysseus, he declared), and in return for his life promised to tell the truth – but instead told the Trojans that the Greeks, trying to make amends for the earlier theft of the Palladium, had built the horse as a propitiatory offering to Athena, to ensure a safe passage home. Secondly, a prodigy occurred which left no doubt: two immense serpents came out of the sea, made straight for Laocoön and his sons, and crushed them to death. This was regarded as a clear sign of the gods' displeasure at Laocoön's irreverent treatment of the Wooden Horse; and with great ceremony the Trojans proceeded to bring it into the city. The story as a whole is well documented, and the action of the Trojans quite explicable, but, even so, the detail about the serpents seems somewhat improbable, and has long awaited a more coherent explanation. . .

The great moment had arrived, our heroes had entered the wooden bowels of the Big Bunny, and those of us not chosen for the exploit had clambered into the hollow ships, to retreat beyond the boundless horizon until the evening should dawn (as it were), when, guided by Venus and the red light from Helen's upper window, we would quietly make our way back to the citadel, the gates of which should then be open. Yet it was with great trepidation that we departed, leaving our heroes to their cramped fate; for by no means could we tell what might become of them. Not until the affair was over did we discover what had happened; and when Odysseus later told the tale our blood ran colder than that of a serpent as we realised how close to total defeat we had been. . .

"It was a dark and stormy night, roaring – I mean, pouring with rain," Odysseus began, "and, as if in Plato's cavern – or Pluto's for that matter – obscure shadows only from the world beyond could be discerned. And a cold time we had of it, you might say – there were times we regretted it, galled, sore-seated, refractory, with bugs in the bunny and voices in our ears, saying that this was all folly. As Machaon, our healer, put it, we'd all had better room and bawd elsewhere – no fa–, I mean, space to fit in; spi–, I mean, little to speak about; a growing desire to siphon the python, as they say in the antipodes; with the boards getting harder and our resolution weaker. Yes, a hard time we had of it.

"And then at dawn the Trojans swarmed out like bees from the hive to behold the marvel and decide what to do about it. From the buzz we gathered that they believed us gone, and that they accepted the gift as their natural right, but were apparently much divided over what to do about it. For the moment the drones consoled themselves with scribbling graffiti on it – 'Orpheus is a lyre', 'Medea for the massage', 'Charybdis sucks', and so on. Even a snatch of poetry:

> Poseidon's serpents come out of the sea,
> They'll catch all the others, but they won't

But with the appearance of Laocoön, Priest of Poseidon, the discussion grew more serious. There might be a catch in it, he seemed to think, but though he couldn't find the opening he went so far as to poke his spear into its belly, crying 'What's up, Doc?' – and only just in time was I able to clap my hand over Machaon's mouth before he could emit more than a hollow groan. Laocoön accepted the bunny as an offering to Athena all right, but he proposed that it be a burnt offering, just in case; and we were scared spitless at the very thought.

"Fortunately, who should come along at that moment but old Sinon – right on cue, just in case of such an emergency. Simple Sinon, we call him, because he gives the impression of being a bit irrational at times – not quite the round pi, you might say. The Trojans seized him triumphantly, and brought him before Laocoön, who looked at him suspiciously. 'Sinon,' he said meanly. 'Sounds like a nasty nasal complaint.' But at least he asked him what he was doing there, and why we'd built the Big Bunny, and so on.

"Well, slippery Sinon put on quite a show for them – he's a master of equivocation – they don't call him Old 'Yes and No' for nothing. And to some extent he was caught between the Trojans and the deep blue sea, so he had very little option – he had to go for the best result

[104]

possible rather than the best possible result, as somebody or another would have it.

So he told them how I'd thrown him out of the team just because he'd once been the partner of Palamedes, and accused me of being a real snake in the grass, as thankless as a serpent's tooth, yellow and dangerous like snark-infested custard, and more of the same. I got quite rattled, and if Machaon hadn't clapped his hand over my mouth just in time we'd have all tasted the worm.

"And then he told them how we'd given up in disgust, leaving the gift for Athena and Poseidon so that they wouldn't zap us on the way home.

Laocoön was somewhat mollified, yet not altogether convinced; but just at that moment Cassandra started screeching for a bonfire, and of course opinion immediately swung round in our favour. Even so, Laocoön obviously didn't want to give up the auto-da-fé idea entirely, and therefore consulted their Oracle (not as good as ours) about the best line of action, only to get the following reply:

Qui legitis flores et humi nascentia fraga,
Frigidus, O pueri, fugite hinc, latet anguis in herba.

Well, nobody could understand that foreign lingo, and the best they could make of it was something about flowers and cold strawberries for anguished boys lurking in the low grass – but then the Oracle popped a few more cogs, and came out with a hand and the appropriate instructions: Sinon, South; Dummy, North; Laocoön, East; Cassandra, West – the contract Four Spades, the lead to be the 5 of diamonds:

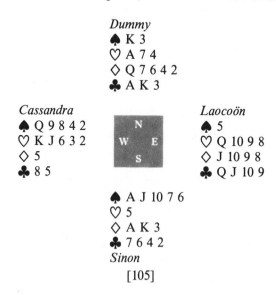

Dummy
♠ K 3
♡ A 7 4
♢ Q 7 6 4 2
♣ A K 3

Cassandra
♠ Q 9 8 4 2
♡ K J 6 3 2
♢ 5
♣ 8 5

Laocoön
♠ 5
♡ Q 10 9 8
♢ J 10 9 8
♣ Q J 10 9

♠ A J 10 7 6
♡ 5
♢ A K 3
♣ 7 6 4 2
Sinon

[105]

"Peeping through the chinks, we watched as Sinon played the hand. The contract looked easy enough as he won the opening lead; but a small spade to the King and another back revealed the bad news – there were potentially three trump losers, and a club – and little hope of constricting the latter without losing control of the hand. Sinon recoiled as if bitten, then, reluctantly, put in the jack and lost to the queen. Back came the feared and forcing heart switch, which Sinon won with the ace; following that with the ace of clubs; and then, as if mesmerised, he played a small club from dummy, looking aghast as he 'realised' what he had done, and 'protesting' vainly that he'd meant to play the king. Laocoön was taken in – not fearing the Greek gift he won the club, and couldn't resist returning another for his partner to ruff; only to find that he'd fallen right into the coils of the Serpent Coup, as Sinon ruffed the heart return, to come down to this position:

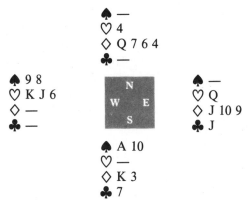

The lead of the trumps now squeezed Laocoön out of existence, and too late did he realize that he should have resisted the wiles of the serpent.

"Sinon had thus proved himself the subtlest beast of the field, and cries of Laocoön and Cassandra were disregarded as with great rejoicing and to the sound of coiled trumpets the Trojans carried us through the gates of Troy. And that is how," Odysseus concluded, "we were able to destroy their dreams of Paradise and scotch their hopes. Such is life in the snakepit – so much depends on little words like 'if' and 'not' – but if Sinon had not spoken with a forked tongue, and if Laocoön had not been tempted by that forbidden fruit, then it would have been us and not them going up in smoke."

XXII

The Greek Gift

Note: The Wooden Horse having been brought within the walls of
Troy, the Greeks hidden within awaited the fall of darkness,
when Sinon would let them out. Meanwhile, guided by a light
from Helen's window and a flame burning upon the tomb of
Achilles, Agamemnon's ships were on their way back, and,
released from the Horse, Odysseus and his men opened the
gates of Troy to the Greek host, and set fire to the citadel.
Taken completely by surprise, the Trojans were unable to
resist their foes, and were quickly subdued. Menelaus and
Odysseus, however, the former anxious to find his wife and
personally put her to the sword (and the latter anxious to see it
done), sought out the spacious house of Deiphobus, whom
Helen had married after the death of Paris. That Menelaus
changed his mind about killing Helen is certain, but the
reasons for that change are many-layered: some say that
Helen, at the critical moment, dropped the sheet that covered
her naked breast, and Menelaus, numbed by the vision of
Beauty, was unable to carry out his intention; other accounts
suggest that Aphrodite intervened to save her favourite; and
yet others say that the apparent presence of Helen of Troy was
an illusion created by the gods (an *eidolon*), and that the real
Helen had been for the duration of the war in Egypt. Unlikely
as it may seem, there is a grain of truth in all these stories, and
what is beyond dispute is the way that, amidst all the disasters
befalling the Trojans at the end, the triumph of Helen over
Menelaus emerges so clearly. . .

"Experience," began Odysseus, as we sat round after the match, "is
the name Menelaus gives to his mistakes, but the only thing that
Menelaus learns from experience is that he learns nothing from
experience – for him, experience is the worst cheater." His words were
bitter, and small wonder, for one blunder by Menelaus had been the
prelude to a number of others, and had cost us any chance of a place
in the Final; and there could be little doubt that Menelaus, by
turning the sublime to the ridiculous, had in every sense given up all
for love.

[107]

For up until that moment everything had gone to plan. Our hidden heroes had hopped out from nowhere, and, catching the unwary Trojans unawares, had compelled them to consent to the resumption of play; and our sea-borne fighters, sailing beneath the friendly silence of the peaceful moon, and guided by the red light of Helen's upper chamber, had also arrived, sweeping all before them as the darkness fell on Troy. But when we met Helen and Deiphobus in one of the later rounds, Agamemnon had decided that Odysseus should go with Menelaus to ensure no weakening of the will. And now, frustrated as the bat which fell in love with the umbrella, Odysseus was forced to admit that he had failed.

"I knew we were in trouble," he continued, "the moment Menelaus began to quote poetry – that 'I can love any, so be she not true' sort of nonsense. And the way he played the first few hands was rather ominous – as the Bard rightly says, 'Troy in our weakness lives, not in her strength'. Apparently he'd been dreaming of her all that night of the dark horse, convinced that she'd come to him in his sleep, and that Aphrodite herself had told him, 'No other can as well espouse her'. He still fancies himself as a ladies' man, despite all the evidence to the contrary. So I had a word with him at the half – we were slightly down – repeating Agamemnon's threat to string us up if we lost, and reminding him of the old saying that the difference between being well-hanged and well-hung is the difference between a peasant and a pheasant, and I didn't want to be either, thank you. For a while it seemed to work, and we appeared to be getting on like a house on fire, but then Board 13 hit the table, and we bit the dust.

"The bidding," he went on, "unlike the later play, was quite normal. Deiphobus opened one heart; Helen responded two diamonds; he rebid three clubs; she three no trumps. And that, as the tautology goes, was that. I was now on lead, and this was my hand:

♠ K Q 10 7 4
♡ 5 3 2
◇ A 6 4
♣ 5 2

Naturally, I led the king of spades, and cursed furiously when dummy came down with three to the jack – in fact, with J 9 2, A Q 9 7 4, singleton 9, and A K Q 9. Now, to my surprise, I found myself holding the trick. My partner, despite his play of the 8, clearly didn't have the ace, so Helen was obviously up to something. Had it been

Menelaus playing, I'd have simply assumed that he'd fouled up a Bath Coup, but Helen's technique has improved immeasurably since she left home, thanks to Paris and Deiphobus – so, inevitable conclusion, the ace of spades must be the only entry to her diamond suit – which I control. The full deal was:

Board 13
All Vulnerable

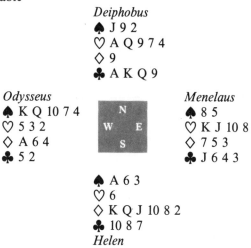

Deiphobus
♠ J 9 2
♡ A Q 9 7 4
◇ 9
♣ A K Q 9

Odysseus
♠ K Q 10 7 4
♡ 5 3 2
◇ A 6 4
♣ 5 2

Menelaus
♠ 8 5
♡ K J 10 8
◇ 7 5 3
♣ J 6 4 3

♠ A 6 3
♡ 6
◇ K Q J 10 8 2
♣ 10 8 7
Helen

"Now, Greeks are supposed to give gifts, not receive them – so when my king held, as quick as silvery Mercury I returned the compliment by playing back the queen, Menelaus looking at me bemusedly as I set up the jack on table – he probably still thinks that's why the contract made. Helen won the ace; then came back the 10 of diamonds, trying to steal a trick, but I hopped up with the ace and exited with a heart. Helen tried the queen, but Menelaus won the king; and then (correctly) returned the jack of hearts. Helen let that hold – I told you her technique has improved – and it was at this point, with us having got all the hard bits right and now needing only one more trick, that everything went wrong:

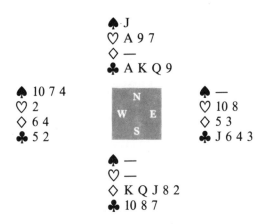

```
              ♠ J
              ♡ A 9 7
              ◊ —
              ♣ A K Q 9

♠ 10 7 4          N          ♠ —
♡ 2           W       E      ♡ 10 8
◊ 6 4             S          ◊ 5 3
♣ 5 2                        ♣ J 6 4 3

              ♠ —
              ♡ —
              ◊ K Q J 8 2
              ♣ 10 8 7
```

"Even Menelaus could see that as long as he returned a heart, then he must make his club in the end. But he hesitated, and was lost, for Helen, turning towards him, deliberately bent over as if to take a closer look at dummy, her chiton falling away; and Menelaus, seeing those topless towers from which he had been banished and recalling past wanderings in Aphrodite's golden grove, was dazzled by the vision of Beauty so unexpectedly revealed. It was Aphrodite and Paris all over again, and Menelaus didn't even try to resist – the play of the heart had to be right; a club would have put Helen to a guess if not the sword; but Menelaus came back a diamond! They say that flagellation is good for the soul, but a switch like that would turn anyone off!

"And that is how," Odysseus concluded gloomily, "Topless Helen pulled off a vulnerable game, her chiton, and a bare-faced swindle in one swift move. And that was us undone completely for the rest of the match. That woman," he added bitterly, "the Wooden Mare of Troy, in whom a score of heroes have slept – as Tiresias says, she's had more hands up her skirts than the muppets, whatever they are. But she can still make a fool of Menelaus – I honestly declare that if she told him she'd been in Egypt instead of Troy for the past ten years he'd probably believe her. And he still wants her back! It's what the henpecked Socrates wryly calls the triumph of hope over experience. I know that in the play of the heart one man's mede is another man's persian, and that monogamy leaves much to be desired – but quite frankly, I've had enough of foreign affairs in this Zeus-forsaken hole, and can't wait to get back to Argos – my dog, that is – and to my faithful wife Penelope."

[110]

XXIII

The Fall of the Trojan King

Note: The topless towers of Ilium aflame, and confusion everywhere
in the broad streets of Troy, the Trojans were no match for the
all-conquering Greeks, who mercilessly put them to the sword
(Aeneas, carrying his father Anchises upon his shoulders,
being one of the few to escape the flames). Many were the
scenes of bloodshed and violence: Aias dragging Cassandra by
the hair from the Temple of Athena (on his way home, he
would be drowned for that profanity); Polyxena, youngest
daughter of Priam, taken to be later sacrificed upon the tomb
of Achilles; and Priam himself, venerable monarch, taking
refuge with his wife Hecuba and youngest son Polites at
the altar of Zeus, where he made a feeble gesture to defend
himself and his family, only to be butchered by the arrogant
Neoptolemus (Pyrrhus). Many are the tales that might be told
of those direful dark days, but the final flourish of the Trojans
forms a worthy conclusion to our mighty epic, pyrrhic victory
though it might have been. . .

So all day long the noise of battle rolled, and one by one the teams
of Troy had fallen to the all-conquering Greeks, leaving only that of
Priam himself to ward off total disaster. And Priam, vulnerable king,
was now left *Solus Rex* amidst the ruins of his former majesty,
disconsolately contemplating the quietus to come.

That they had even made it to the Final was miracle enough, and
one due mainly to the heroic endeavours of pious Aeneas, who,
unable to stay till the end, had made himself available only for the
team which nobody had expected to survive. But now he had gone
("I'm off to pick up the old man," he had said. "We're off to Rome
and places, and the boat's already waiting – pleasure before duty, and
all that. Sorry I can't stay."); and Priam, sadly reflecting that as we
get older we do not get any younger, had sent off the callipygian
couple, Cassandra and Polyxena, to the Athena Room, and was now
waiting in the closed room beside the statue of Zeus for the coming of
the Greeks.

Their hopes of Elysium, he knew, were far from happy – the girls

[111]

were bound to be carried off and slaughtered, and that morning's *Evangelos*, assessing their chances, had reckoned it would be easier for a camel to pass through the knee of an idol. And when she heard that Priam himself had elected to take arms Hecuba was most troubled, pointing out how bad the stress would be for his heart condition; but Priam, having little choice, had determined to accept the stroke of Fate with dignity, and to go down fighting.

Where were they, he wondered, gazing idly at the altar of Zeus and suddenly seeing a faded inscription that he'd never before noticed. Hoping for a favourable omen, he was further disheartened to make out a broken and incomplete message, and one that boded further ill – 'Deteriorata', it was headed, and his scratching finger deciphered a few more phrases – 'crawl abject amidst the noise and the bustle . . . you are a fluke of the universe . . . you have no right to be here'.

Life, he thought, as he disconsolately took his seat again, the hidden secret at the end of the universe – oh, to be 42 again. He sent Polites off to look for the opposition, but Hecuba remained, knitting as usual (even though most of the kids have gone, he reflected), and talking about the Symposium they'd be having tomorrow, when it was all over. If there is a tomorrow, he thought gloomily. And he thought back to those early days of love – the first careless rapture. She had been some looker then – perhaps a few microhelens short of perfection, but those legs . . . then . . . and now . . . "Barely soup," she was saying, "and horse à la carte, with glib tongue and blue-veined cheese. . ."

With a guilty start he raised his eyes from her legs as she changed the subject. "Where's Polites?" she asked. "My little boy. He should be back by now."

"You worry too much about him," he heard himself saying. "You'll give the lad a complex. He's eighteen years old, and a manly fellow, but you still treat him like a baby."

"Oedipus-schmiedipus," she replied, "and he-man-Schliemann, for that matter. If a boy loves his mother there'll always be a Troy."

At that moment Polites returned, with the news that Neoptolemus and Philoctetes were on their way. And the next moment the doors burst open, and the two greasy Greeks swaggered to their seats. Well-mannered Polites, as always the perfect gentlemen, greeted them in courteous manner, and offered refreshment before the game should begin: "My dear Philoctetes, my dear Pyrrhus, how nice to see you – what about the cup that cheers – how do you take it?"; but Neoptolemus, irritated by being called Pyrrhus, rudely retorted,

[112]

"How would you like your head – one lump or two?" It was obviously not going to be a friendly encounter.

They were irritated, it seemed, because they'd wanted to play the girls ("Wouldn't mind being the destiny that shaped those ends," muttered Philoctetes, obscurely); but Agamemnon had refused them that pleasure. And when he'd made his usual "win-their-hearts-and-minds" inspiratory speech, Neoptolemus had incurred his great commander's wrath – and hence the delay – by loudly retorting that if you grabbed 'em by the short-and-curlies their hearts and minds would follow – advice which Aias was presently following in the other room. And Polites's mannerisms annoyed him, true son of his father, being the sort of refinement that invites coarseness in the beholder – and when it came to coarseness, few would wish to behold Neoptolemus. Achilles would have been proud of him, the way he'd changed from a lad to a lout in such a short time!

As expected, the match was an unmitigated disaster for Priam and Polites, who were completely ineffectual throughout; the times indeed required better defenders. Yet when the final hand hit the table Priam felt that at last he had the chance of striking a feeble blow in reply; but Neoptolemus brushed aside a pre-emptive three clubs as though it were a gnat, and grunted his way to a rather sweaty small slam in diamonds:

Board 39
All Vulnerable

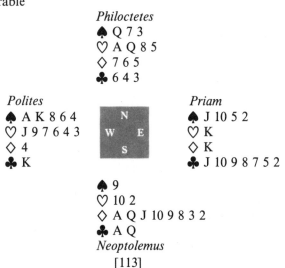

Philoctetes
♠ Q 7 3
♡ A Q 8 5
◇ 7 6 5
♣ 6 4 3

Polites
♠ A K 8 6 4
♡ J 9 7 6 4 3
◇ 4
♣ K

Priam
♠ J 10 5 2
♡ K
◇ K
♣ J 10 9 8 7 5 2

♠ 9
♡ 10 2
◇ A Q J 10 9 8 3 2
♣ A Q
Neoptolemus

[113]

The inexperience of Polites showed when, having cashed his king of spades, he switched to the king of clubs, his partner's suit. Neoptolemus, with a contemptuous "Huh!", won the trick; played the ace of diamonds, dropping the king; and then said coarsely to Priam, "No sense wasting good drinking time. If you've got one or more hearts with the king, I'm one down; otherwise I claim."

Priam, looking at his singleton king of hearts, disputed the claim, insisting that the line stated committed Neoptolemus to the finesse. Neoptolemus looked at him in contempt, asking if he'd never heard of a count squeeze, but knowing that it had been a massacre anyway conceded one down with the comment, "No use arguing – we'll miss out on too much rape and pillage."

And after they'd gone, Priam looked ruefully at his ruined score-card, and sighed, "Well, at least that's one good board." But Polites, who had been looking thoughtful, replied that, on the contrary, it was the final insult, a pyrrhic victory in every sense. When asked to explain, he showed what would happen when the queen of clubs was cashed, and six more diamonds run, to create the following position:

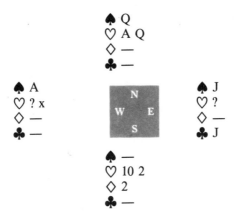

"And when the last diamond is led," he concluded, "West has to throw his x of hearts, dummy the queen of spades, and East whatever he likes. And then a small heart is played to the ace – since West is marked with the ace of spades, his other card by simple logic is either the king of hearts or it isn't; and either way up goes the ace and down comes the king. Axiomatic, my dear Euclid – not even a hypothesis, just a bit of simple addition – but it's put us out for the count."

Priam struggled to his feet, the blood pounding in his veins, but this final disclosure was too much for a heart already broken – the last careless rupture, he thought. He fell upon the altar steps, a mist descending before his eyes; and as a long and worthy life died into darkness the words of the immortal Bard flickered through his fading consciousness:

> To bid, or not to bid, that is the question.
> Whether 'tis nobler in the mind to suffer
> Th'abuse and invective of outragèd partner,
> By taking out his harmful crazy doubles,
> Or by defending, leave them? To pass, to bid?
> To bid perchance to game – ay, there's the rubber,
> For in that dream of slam what breaks may come
> When we have shuffled up the foolish pack,
> Or from this hollow ship of mortal fools?
> Out, out, brief candle! the game's not worth thy shadow.
> We strut and fret our hour about the table,
> And then may bid no more. 'Tis a pastime played
> By idiots full of sickly resolution,
> Signifying nothing. . .

And the rest, we know, is silence.

XXIV

The Lamentable Tragedy of the Trojan Women

Note: After the fall of Troy, the city was put to the torch and most of
its inhabitants to the sword; but the women of Troy, destined
to be slaves and concubines for their Greek conquerors, were
gathered on the shore, lamenting their fate. Four of them, in
particular, had much to lament: Hecuba, wife of Priam, whose
husband and sons had all been slaughtered, and who had been
allotted to Odysseus; Cassandra, deranged daughter of
Hecuba, who, given the power of prophecy by Apollo, was
also fated never to be believed, and whose earlier warnings of
the destruction of Troy had gone unheeded, as would her
later predictions of the deaths of Aias and Agamemnon;
Andromache, widow of Hector and future concubine of
Neoptolemus, whose baby son Astyanax would be pitched from
the walls of Ilium lest he grow up to avenge his father; and
Helen, who, having turned to Deiphobus for consolation after
the death of Paris, was now to return to Sparta with her
husband Menelaus. By strange coincidence, the Fates were to
deal the identical hand in the year 1931 of another era, when
John S. Bennett, a perfume salesman of Kansas City, was shot
by his wife Myrtle for going down in the same contract (with
the same bidding and leads) that Helen, some 3,000 years
earlier, had played to defend her reputation. We now present
the first proper edition of this long-lost play. . .

CHORUS:

While Troy burns, and the smoke from its fiery towers
Rises to the topless heavens, we, the poor, the poor women of
Troy,
Living and partly living, are gathered here upon this tumid
beach,[1]
Awaiting our Greek captors, who will take us back to Argos.[2]

1. There is at this point in the manuscript an almost indecipherable gloss, obviously
Greek in origin, which can only be construed as 'Tits olé' – a gratuitous and
lamentable lapse of taste which forms a near-mockery of our dramatist's earn-est
toil.
2. The country, that is.

[116]

As here we sit, our hearts and minds won o'er by curling Fate,[3]   [5]
Our futures subject to a destiny which cannot be revoked,
Our lamentation rises to the gods who dealt this rotten state.
As here we wait the turning of both time and tide,
As our masters stuff the bellies of their hollow ships,
Before we board, poor Queens, to go our chequered ways –[4]   [10]
Some to bed with Kings, but others to fall to Knaves –
We turn on Helen, only begetter of all this misery:
Though she may justify the ways of gods to Menelaus,
Her words weigh most unjustly on such menless folk as us.

HECUBA:

My love has sicklied into loath,   [15]
And foul seems all that fair I fancied.
The lily seems a leprous growth,
The very buttercups are rancid.[5]

Helen, j'accuse! The flower of Troy gone west.
Destroyer of our men, our ships, our cities.   [20]
A thousand heroes slain, torn each noble breast;
Five hundred women gone – a thousand pities.[6]

Who would weep for Hecuba! 'Tis always thus –
Our tears must ever thin the wine-dark seas.
And I flung forth with foul Odysseus –   [25]
We bed with dogs, we rise with fleas.

CHORUS: ALL:

The mobled queen runs barefoot up and down,
Threat'ning the flames with blood and thunder;
While Helen and her husband, queen and clown,
Look on in majesty and awful wonder.   [30]
The play's the thing! – Let topless Helen frown!
And may she go down with dismal thud and blunder,
Ditched by her husband, and stripped of her crown –
What the gods have put together, we women shall tear asunder.

3. An unusual epithet, since Opportunity, they say, is bald, and cannot easily be seized.
4. A flagging metaphor, drawn from inferior activities.
5. A stanza not altogether lacking in Punch.
6. The gratuitous gloss in the manuscript (see Note 1) is perhaps explained, though the imbalance of heroes to women is still to be deplored.

STROPHE:

[35]
> O King of a very fine nation,
> Why do you lower your station?
> Making love in a ditch
> To – I won't say a bitch,
> But a lady of no reputation.

ANTISTROPHE:

[40]
> Menelaus of very high station,
> Why do you trouble your nation?
> Making love to a bitch
> In – I won't say a ditch,
> But terrain of a low elevation.

ALL:

[45]
Was this the bitch who ditched a thousand ships,
And burnt the topless towers?
Sweet Helen, wouldst thou rank higher than the lowest pips,
This play must prove thy powers.

CASSANDRA:

[50]
> Fortunes rise, fortunes fall.
> Things go from bed to verse.
> Io, Hymen – Hymenaeus –
> And as I deal I curse.

[In which the fair
Cassandra distributes
the pattern of Fate]

[55]
> Young Aias who took me by the hair,
> Agamemnon, mighty King –
> Death by water both shall fear –
> Of a Myrtle wreath I sing.

[In which she tells
of those who have
abused her]

[Fortunes rise, etc.]

[60]
> All slimy things that horrid crawl
> The ocean's floor for meat
> Shall suck him till his bones shall fall
> About his fleshless feet.

[In which the drowning
of Aias in cold water
surf is advertised]

[118]

[Fortunes rise, etc.]

Ruin seize thee, ashen King!
   Confusion in thy bath-tub wait!
In hot water thou mayst sing,
   Thy plug is pulled by Fate.

[In which Agamemnon
   urns his oats]

[Fortunes rise, etc.]

And John S. Bennett, seller of scent,
   Has gone about as far as he can go.
His Saturday Night Special leaves
          him spent,
   And he too shoots below.

[In which everything   [65]
is brought up to date
   in Kansas City]

Fortunes high, and fortunes low.
   Things go from bed to verse.
History repeats her nightmare show –
   This stinking deal is cursed.

[In which the fatal
  outcome to follow   [70]
   is anticipated]

CHORUS:

   Come, players, come, adorn the green baize table!⁷
   Destiny has bid – respond as ye are able.
   Loving not, hating not, just choosing so –   [75]
   The gods set the odds, and with them we must go.
   All things they order in one great cosmic dance –
   They orchestrate the moment, yet still we have our chance.
   Fate deals the cards, but we must play the hands:
   Helen, come forth, seize Fortune where she stands.   [80]

7. The following lines, it has been pointed out, bear an unfortunate resemblance to
Locke's 'Rape of the Pope', but since such apparent imitations may occur by
chance, the coincidence need not greatly concern our understanding.

Board 13
All Vulnerable

Hecuba
♠ A 10 6 3
♡ 10 8 5
◇ 4
♣ A 9 8 4 2

Andromache
♠ Q 7 2
♡ A J 3
◇ A Q 10 9 2
♣ J 6

Cassandra
♠ 4
♡ Q 9 4
◇ K J 7 6 3
♣ Q 7 5 3

```
      N
  W       E
      S
```

♠ K J 9 8 5
♡ K 7 6 2
◇ 8 5
♣ K 10
Helen

Helen looks at her hand,
She knows it's not grand,
And yet she's unable to pass.
'One spade' is the bid,
And it's lifted the lid
Off a canful of snakes in the grass.

[85]

Andromache's next,
And she's rather vexed,
A double might not be wrong.
But then she decides,
By the rules she abides –
'Two diamonds' – the end of her song.

[90]

Hecuba's turn –
Will she never learn?
She's met light openings before.
'Three spades' must be right,
It could even go light –
But no, she leaps right into 4.

[95]

Cassandra to call,
It's vulnerable all –   [100]
The odds must favour the pass.
Like flies and like fleas
Are those 4's and those 3's –
She'd surely fall flat on her knees.[8]

ANDROMACHE:

O Helen, thou hast one brief game to make,   [105]
Or else must thou go down perpetually:
From the fury of scorned women to Hades shalt thou flee,
From the nightmare of history, ne'er shalt thou awake.

O lente, lente currite, noctis equi [nal],[9]
Time's arrow wounds all heels and finds its mark: [110]
My bouncing baby boy told to push off in the dark,
And Hector, mighty horseman, has played his final final.

Time's arrow once released may not be recalled,
Nor door of stable bolted when once the horse has flown:
Within the egg of Leda, the fearful future sown,   [115]
Within the wooden mare, our destiny enthralled.

The night of the dark horse has left its mark on me,
But, Leda's daughter, my lead shall e'er daunt thee.

CHORUS: ALL:

As bats through the dark streets of Troy
Flit thoughts through Andromache's mind.   [120]
Epic perplexity governs her choice —
What sort of lead shall she find?

8. Although the metrical pattern is apparently violated here (though some scholars
would argue for it as a rare example of the long-tailed triplet to close the scene), no
obvious emendation springs to mind. And the dangers of so doing are exemplified
by Pope's *Dunciad* III.27–28, where scorn is poured upon Theobald's proposed
substitution of 'years' for 'ears' in the following lines:
      Wond'ring he gaz'd: When lo! a Sage appears,
      By his broad shoulders known, and length of ears.
Not (we must hasten to add) that 'ears' has any relevance in the present context.
9. 'Run slowly, nightmares' – the sombre Ovidian or Faustian echo marred only by the
need for emendation ['equinal'] to ensure the correct rhyme scheme (but what, as
Lewis Carroll might say, is the use of a scholarly edition without footnotes and at
least one new reading [see, however, Note 8]).

	STROPHE	ANTISTROPHE
	No second Troy	Unlike the Phoenix
	Will rise from the ash	Of splendour and fame
[125]	No sons of great Priam	No daughter of Leda
	With valour and dash	Shall form in the flame.
	We call for a hero	That's for the birds
	A kingdom, a horse	Of a quite different colour –
	And then into battle	Like swans into song stirred
[130]	Too late, of course –	Our valour's now pallor.

ALL:

Lest Apollo be mad at our song,
And we be like Marsyas flayed,
We won't make the agony long –
The Ace of diamonds is played.

HELEN:

[135]
The ace is played, the dummy laid
Upon the green baize table.
Oh partner why did you bid so high?
In spades my hopes are sable.

She wins the trick – oh, what a shame –
[140]
The knave of clubs to follow.
I win the king, yet ca'no' sing –
It all seems rather hollow.

A small trump then – I try the ten
(Perhaps that's rather witless?) –
[145]
But when it stands, the king to hand
(I was scared rather spitless).

The diamond ruffed, or I'd be down –[10]
So far all is grand.
The club ace holds, the 9 unfolds –
[150]
Anagnorisis is at hand.[11]

10. In Greek drama, *hamartia* or the tragic flaw, without which drama lacks human complexity. The contract is cold if Helen simply draws the last trump and plays on clubs. The premature diamond ruff has cost a vital entry.
11. In Greek drama, the crucial moment of recognition. If Cassandra does not cover, Andromache will ruff; and dummy's clubs will be wasted for lack of an entry.

[122]

The moment of nemesis, or parthenogenesis –
Cassandra plays the queen!
Had she ducked, then I'd be lost –
That would be most obscene.

Andromache's play – if she throws away   [155]
The final spade I'll draw;
If she over-trumps she's on her rump –
An end-play exceedingly sore.

And either way I win the day,
The last two clubs are good.   [160]
The contract made – tereu, tirade,
As they say in the Sacred Wood.[12]

CHORUS:

In vain, in vain, 'tis not otherwise but thus –
Helen is triumphant, our raised hopes razed to dust.
Huddled on this tumid shore, we poor women make our moan;   [165]
Every dogma has its day, and every bitch her bone.
She, once an ugly duckling, should have been exposed;
The gods, it seems, think otherwise, and have their plans disclosed.
'Life is just a message scribbled in the dark' – Anon.
Our virtue but a bubble – one prick, forever gone.   [170]
What is past is past, nor can the future be undone –
The black ships now are ready, our greasy masters come.
Would they but take the women, and leave the girls behind
(Callipygian thoughts, alas, are foremost in their mind).
Destiny shapes our ends, though we with contracts toy;   [175]
Babylonian darkness will soon blot the town of Troy.
And like the fabled bird of Egypt, flying round and round,
We move in small concentric circles, just above the ground,
Till when the Last Trump's played, in one sad desperate Fall,
We're sucked into the last Black Hole, and darkness covers all.   [180]

12. In Greek drama, *hubris*, or fatal pride. But in the organisation of these critical
moments we find evidence to suggest that our unknown dramatist cannot be
ranked with the finest tragedians – the moment of *hubris* should always precede
that of *anagnorisis*; here, the protagonist seems not to have obtained any insight
into her manifest failings, and the moral force of the drama is accordingly less
powerful. Indeed, the cry of the nightingale ['tereu' intimating profane sexuality, if
not prostitution] seems to be a calculated thumbing of the nose, as it were, at the
Virgins of the Sacred Wood (among whom, one must not forget, is Cassandra).

[123]

Epilogue

Our tale is told, our end is cold. . . etc. . . . More could be said of the Homecoming – Odysseus stopping off for a few and getting back late (not that Penelope had all that much to show for so long at the loom, mind you!); Agamemnon laid out flat when he tried to bring ditto Cassandra home; yours truly getting back to a 'Dear Di' epistle. . . Attached as we are to them, these are other tales.

And more could be said of the pain of its birth – hide of the goat, ink of the squid, quill of the grey goose, midnight toil of the owl. . . . The search for a title – *Priapus Unbound, or The Minstrel's Last Lay*, perhaps? *Topless Helen, or A Sale*, sorry, *A Tale of Two Cities*, maybe? Lacking the authentic touch. . . Then the discouraging responses of Procrustes & Co., Publishers ("we will lose no time reading it. . . we have nothing but praise"). . . And the scorn of various Shining Wits, its general neglect by all – Poetry and Poverty, the Shivering Sisters most truly are they called.

All this was a long time ago, I remember, that Troy passed away in one high funeral gleam – but set this down, set this down. . . We were there, we saw many things, and understood fewer, but in our humble way we have tried to recapture some of those sunlit hours spent in a vanished world. . . Enough! Life may be long, but art need not be so. Finished now – time to set the sheets afloat, to launch them on an unsuspecting world – who can foresee the strange strand where they may beach?

> Go, little Book,
> Tell in glorious rhyme
> As roses might, in magic amber laid,
> Make concrete of the sands of time. . .

No – inspiration sinks, the spark of wit is watered down. Our muse drags her skirts, the pen is at the bottom of the page (or should that be vice-versa – our callipygian swan-song, as it were?). . . Tired now, getting confused – dark ages will soon be the good old days. . . *Erat Hora!* – Time's up. . . Time to blow out the brief candle and shuffle off the stage. . . Good body, every night. . . and may the gods smile on all your finesses. . .

[124]